# MONOGRAPHS ON THE PHYSICS AND CHEMISTRY OF MATERIALS

*General Editors*
B. CHALMERS
WILLIS JACKSON   H. FRÖHLICH   N. F. MOTT

*This series is intended to summarize the recent results in academic or long-range research in materials and allied subjects, in a form that should be useful to physicists in Government and industrial laboratories*

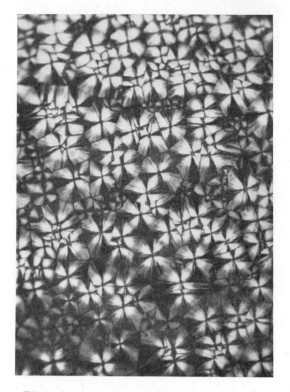

Film of polyethylene viewed between crossed Nicols, showing 'spherulitic clusters' of crystallites. (Bunn and Alcock.)

# THE PHYSICS OF
# RUBBER ELASTICITY

BY

## L. R. G. TRELOAR
BRITISH RUBBER PRODUCERS'
RESEARCH ASSOCIATION

OXFORD
AT THE CLARENDON PRESS
1949

*Oxford University Press, Amen House, London E.C. 4*

GLASGOW NEW YORK TORONTO MELBOURNE WELLINGTON
BOMBAY CALCUTTA MADRAS CAPE TOWN

*Geoffrey Cumberlege, Publisher to the University*

PRINTED IN GREAT BRITAIN

# PREFACE

It is sometimes considered unnecessary for those engaged in the practical development of industrial processes to concern themselves with the so-called theoretical aspects of their subject. On examination, it is usually found that exponents of this point of view are not entirely consistent, for in any type of work involving experimentation it is impossible to get along without some sort of theory, however limited or *ad hoc* it may be. My excuse for doing the work which I do (of which this book is one aspect) is that I always believe that if one is going to have a theory at all one may as well take some trouble to find the one which most nearly represents the known facts.

In the subject of rubber elasticity it is not easy to discover from the mass of literature, often of a rather mathematical character, what are the generally accepted theories. In this book I have therefore attempted to convey (in not too mathematical language) the fundamental concepts of the subject, and to present the whole in a more or less consistent form. In this task I have admittedly given expression to my own point of view, and I have drawn freely on the work of my associates at the British Rubber Producers' Research Association. I cannot hope to acknowledge the many who have helped me by the discussion of particular sections, but I should like to mention particularly Dr. G. Gee, Director of the B.R.P.R.A., who read and criticized the manuscript in detail, my colleague Mr. R. S. Rivlin, who gave me the benefit of his unpublished ideas and works, and Dr. K. Weissenberg, with whom I was able to discuss the final chapter.

I should also like to thank the Board of the B.R.P.R.A. for encouraging me to undertake this work, and for the provision of facilities for its execution.

L. R. G. T.

BRITISH RUBBER PRODUCERS'
RESEARCH ASSOCIATION
WELWYN GARDEN CITY

# ACKNOWLEDGEMENTS

THE author wishes to thank the following for permission to use figures in this book:

The Faraday Society for Figs. 2.8, 2.10, 5.1, 5.2, 5.3, 5.5, 5.6, 6.9, 6.10, 8.5, 8.6, 8.8, 9.8, 9.9, 9.10, 9.11, 10.1, and 10.2, C. W. Bunn and the Faraday Society for the Frontispiece, the Physical Society for Figs. 7.2, 7.3, 7.4, 8.9, and 8.10, Miss D. G. Fisher and the Physical Society for Fig. 9.1, the Institution of the Rubber Industry for Figs. 11.4, 11.5, and 11.8, L. Mullins and the Institution of the Rubber Industry for Figs. 12.1 and 12.2, K. H. Meyer and the Editor of *Helvetica Chimica Acta*, for Figs. 2.1 and 2.4, W. Kuhn and the Editor of *Helvetica Chimica Acta* for Fig. 6.6, E. Guth and the Editor of the *Journal of Physical Chemistry* for Figs. 2.5 and 2.6, E. Guth and the American Chemical Society for Fig. 2.12, L. A. Wood and the American Institute of Physics for Figs. 2.9, 2.10, and 9.5, L. A. Wood and the American Chemical Society for Figs. 9.3 and 9.7, L. A. Wood and Interscience Publishers for Fig. 9.4, H. Benoît and the Société de Chimie physique for Fig. 3.4, G. Gee and the Editor of the *Journal of Polymer Science* for Figs. 5.8, 10.5, and 10.6, P. J. Flory and the American Chemical Society for Figs. 5.9, 10.3, and 10.4, N. Bekkedahl and the American Bureau of Standards for Figs. 9.2 and 9.6, J. E. Field and the American Institute of Physics for Fig. 9.12, J. M. Goppel and the Editor of *Applied Scientific Research* for Fig. 9.13, A. J. Wildschut and the Elsevier Publishing Company for Fig. 10.8, H. Eyring and the American Institute of Physics for Fig. 11.6, H. Eyring and the American Chemical Society for Fig. 11.7, A. V. Tobolsky and the American Institute of Physics for Figs. 11.9, 11.10, and 11.11 A. P. Aleksandrov and the Soviet Academy of Sciences for Figs. 12.4 and 12.6, S. D. Gehman and the American Chemical Society for Fig. 12.8, J. H. Dillon and the American Institute of Physics for Figs. 12.9 and 12.10, and R. S. Rivlin and the American Institute of Physics for Fig. 13.5.

# CONTENTS

# CHAPTER I

# GENERAL PHYSICAL PROPERTIES OF RUBBERS

## 1. Introduction

THE word 'rubber' is used in two different senses. Originally it meant 'india-rubber', the natural product of the tree *Hevea Braziliensis*, of which the chief chemical constituent is the rubber hydrocarbon $(C_5H_8)_n$ or polyisoprene. The only other rubber then known was *gutta-percha* or *balata*, another natural product represented by the same empirical formula $(C_5H_8)_n$, but differing slightly in the structural form of the molecule. Recent years have seen the development of a very large number of synthetic rubbers having a wide variety of chemical constitutions, and the term 'rubber' is now commonly employed to include any material comparable with natural rubber in possessing the physical property of large elastic extensibility. Some writers prefer to restrict the word to its original usage, and to employ some other term, such as 'synthetic elastomer', to designate members of the more general class. However, in the present work the more popular usage will be followed. It will generally be obvious from the context whether the word rubber is used in the general or in the particular sense; in cases where confusion might arise, it will be sufficient to refer to *natural* or *Hevea* rubber.

The reasons for this choice are not entirely verbal. It is at least equally justifiable from a scientific point of view to define rubber in terms of its physical properties as in terms of its chemical constitution. Indeed, in the present work we shall be concerned very much more with the fundamental structural aspects in which all rubbers may be considered to be essentially the same, than with the more detailed specific features in which they differ from one another. The emphasis will be placed mainly on *rubber-like elasticity* as a phenomenon associated with the *rubber-like state of matter*, a state which, as we shall see, is closely related to a certain rather special type of molecular structure.

The most obvious, and also the most important, characteristic of the rubber-like state is, of course, a high degree of elastic deformability under the action of comparatively small stresses. A typical stress-strain curve for rubber is shown in Fig. 1.1; the maximum extensibility normally falls within the range 500

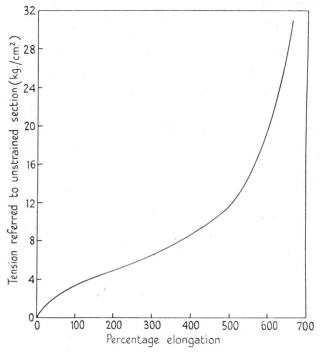

FIG. 1.1. Typical force-extension curve for vulcanized rubber.

to 1,000 per cent., while the value of Young's modulus (in the region of small extensions) is of the order of 10 kg./cm.² or $10^7$ dynes/cm.² By way of contrast it may be mentioned that Young's modulus for typical hard solids is in the region of $10^{12}$ dynes/cm.², while their maximum elastic (i.e. reversible) extensibility seldom exceeds 1 per cent. There is thus an enormous difference between rubbers on the one hand and ordinary hard solids (e.g. of a crystalline or glassy nature) on the other. The interpretation of this difference is the principal question with which this book will be concerned.

## 2. Chemical constitution of rubbers

As already stated, natural rubber is essentially a hydrocarbon having the empirical formula $(C_5H_8)_n$. The hydrocarbon exists in the original latex in the form of small globules of mean diameter about $0.5\,\mu$ ($5.10^{-5}$ cm.) suspended in a watery medium

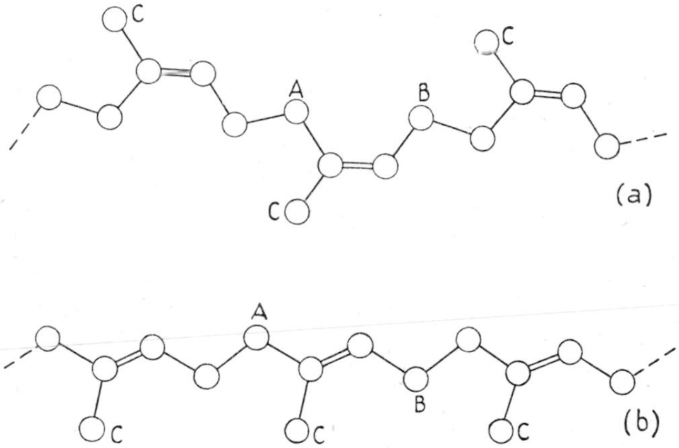

FIG. 1.2.   The structure of the molecule of (a) *Hevea* rubber, and (b) gutta-percha.   *AB*—isoprene unit.   *C*—methyl group.

or serum, the concentration of hydrocarbon being about 35 per cent. of the total weight. The hydrocarbon particles would, of course, coalesce, were it not for a layer or sheath of non-rubber constituents, principally proteins, which is adsorbed on their surfaces and functions as a protective colloid. From this latex the solid rubber may be obtained either by drying off the water or by precipitation with acid. The latter treatment yields the purer rubber, since it leaves most of the non-rubber constituents in the serum.

Chemically, the rubber hydrocarbon is a polymer of isoprene $(C_5H_8)$, built up in the form of a continuous chain, having the structure shown in Fig. 1.2 (a). Every fourth bond in the chain is a double bond, and every fourth carbon atom has attached to it the methyl $(CH_3)$ group, in a perfectly regular manner. The presence of the double bond is very significant, since it is this that largely determines the chemical reactivity of the molecule. It leads at once to the principal advantage and also to the principal disadvantage of natural rubber. The advantage is that it may readily be combined with sulphur, to form the technically much more valuable *vulcanized* rubber. The disadvantage is that it is subject to oxidation, particularly in the presence of light, and this leads to a deterioration of strength and the well-known symptoms of cracking or perishing.

Unlike low-molecular compounds, polymers of very high molecular weight do not usually form molecules containing a uniquely determined number of atoms. Instead, the molecular weights, or chain lengths, are distributed in a statistical manner about a mean value, which in the case of natural rubber is about 350,000. This means that the rubber chain contains, on the average, about 5,000 isoprene units. It is very probable that these units are arranged end to end to form a single unbranched chain. Taking the usual values of bond lengths, the mean length of the molecule on this basis is found to be about $2 \cdot 10^{-4}$ cm.

The structure of gutta-percha differs but slightly from that of rubber. As will be seen from Fig. 1.2 (*b*), the difference lies solely in the arrangement of the single C—C bonds adjacent to the double bond. In natural rubber these single bonds both lie on the *same* side of the double bond, thus $\diagdown\underline{\phantom{xx}}\diagup$, forming the so-called *cis*-configuration, whilst in gutta the single bonds lie on opposite sides of the double bond, thus $\diagdown\diagup\diagdown$, to form the *trans*-configuration. This difference leads to certain differences in physical properties—notably in the phenomena of crystallization—between the two compounds.

Although the two single bonds adjacent to the double bond remain permanently fixed in a single plane (whether in the *cis*- or *trans*-configuration), the remaining single bonds are not thus fixed but are subject to rotation out of the plane formed by neighbouring bonds, as will be discussed in detail later. The structural forms shown in Fig. 1.2 are thus to a certain extent schematic; in practice the molecule does not lie all in one plane, as there suggested.

*Synthetic rubbers*

It is not the purpose of this book to discuss the peculiarities of synthetic rubbers in any detail, but this introduction would not be complete without some reference to this important and expanding group of industrial materials.

The chemical structure of a few of the more important synthetics is shown in Table I. Polychloroprene is a special-

TABLE I

*Structural formulae of some typical rubbers and related materials*

| Structure | Name |
|---|---|
| $-CH_2-\overset{\overset{\displaystyle CH_3}{\mid}}{C}=CH-CH_2-$ | Polyisoprene (natural rubber, gutta-percha) |
| $-CH_2-CH_2-CH_2-CH_2-$ | Polyethylene ('Polythene') |
| $-CH_2-\overset{\overset{\displaystyle Cl}{\mid}}{CH}=CH-CH_2-$ | Polychloroprene ('Neoprene') |
| $-CH_2-\overset{\overset{\displaystyle Cl}{\mid}}{CH}-CH_2-\overset{\overset{\displaystyle Cl}{\mid}}{CH}-$ | Polyvinyl chloride |
| $-CH_2-\underset{\underset{\displaystyle CH_3}{\mid}}{\overset{\overset{\displaystyle CH_3}{\mid}}{C}}-CH_2-\underset{\underset{\displaystyle CH_3}{\mid}}{\overset{\overset{\displaystyle CH_3}{\mid}}{C}}-$ | Polyisobutylene (basis of 'Butyl' rubber) |
| $-NH-\underset{\underset{\displaystyle R}{\mid}}{\overset{\overset{\displaystyle R}{\mid}}{CH}}-CO-NH-CH-CO-$ | Protein (gelatin, wool, silk, etc.) |
| $-CH_2-CH-CH_2-CH-$ (with phenyl rings) | Polystyrene |
| $-CH_2-CH=CH-CH_2-CH_2-CH-$ (with phenyl ring) | Butadiene-styrene interpolymer (German 'Buna-S', American 'GR-S') |
| $-CH_2-\underset{\underset{\displaystyle COOCH_3}{\mid}}{\overset{\overset{\displaystyle CH_3}{\mid}}{C}}-CH_2-\underset{\underset{\displaystyle COOCH_3}{\mid}}{\overset{\overset{\displaystyle CH_3}{\mid}}{C}}-CH_2-$ | Polymethyl methacrylate ('Perspex') |

purpose rubber, which has the property of not swelling to any serious extent in hydrocarbon oils, which makes it particularly useful for engine mountings and similar purposes. It is also very resistant to deterioration by oxygen in the presence of light. Polyvinyl chloride is harder and less extensible than natural rubber; it is widely used in articles of clothing and drapery, where it has the added advantage of showing up coloured pigments very favourably. It is also frequently employed in cable insulation. Butyl rubber, based on polyisobutylene, has the advantage of a lower permeability to gases than natural rubber, which makes it useful for the inner tubes of tyres; against this, however, it does not retain its elasticity at low temperatures so well as natural rubber. GR-S rubber, the general purpose synthetic produced in very large quantities in America during the war, is a mixed polymer of butadiene and styrene. In almost all properties it is inferior to natural rubber, but it can be produced in large quantities at a competitive price.

The formulae in Table I represent only short segments of the molecules, which in all cases have the form of very long chains containing many thousands of monomer units.

## 3. Early theories of rubber elasticity

Reference was made in § 1 to the very wide gap between the elastic properties of rubbers and those of an ordinary hard solid —a difference amounting to a factor of about 100,000 in rigidity and about 1,000 to 10,000 in extensibility. To those who first began to study the reason for these differences it seemed that the only means available for explaining such a large elastic extensibility without departing from classical conceptions of the nature of elasticity was to postulate some sort of open structure which would permit of comparatively large bulk displacements being obtained with only small strains in the structural elements. Familiar examples of such structures are the coil spring and certain types of lattice (or cellular) structures. Theories of rubber elasticity based on models of this kind were proposed, for example, by Ostwald (1926), and by Fikentscher and Mark (1930). Ostwald imagined the outer sheath of the latex globule to be comprised of a sort of network of micelles or molecular aggregates containing protein and resin which was suspended in low-molecular rubber hydrocarbon of a more or less fluid character. The elasticity of the rubber was supposed to be due to the micellar network of non-rubber constituents. Fikentscher and Mark postulated a spiral configuration of the molecule of the rubber hydrocarbon in which the tendency to retract was considered to be due to residual forces between neighbouring turns of the spiral, associated particularly with the double bonds.

A rather similar theory proposed by Mack (1934) envisaged a folded configuration of the polyisoprene molecule maintained by the agency of forces between hydrogen atoms. This model permitted an extension of 300 per cent. in passing from the closely packed to the fully extended form of the chain by rotation about single bonds. In addition, a further extension of the bulk rubber was introduced by turning of the extended molecules into the direction of the strain, bringing the maximum extensibility of the rubber up to 600 per cent.

Mack's theory came very close to current conceptions of elasticity firstly in drawing attention to the possibility of a more or less irregularly kinked form of molecular chain resulting from rotations about single bonds, and secondly by the significance attached to the turning of the molecules into the direction of the extension. The theory was inadequate, however, in regarding the interatomic forces as fundamentally responsible for the elasticity.

## 4. The kinetic theory of elasticity

These theories, and others of a similar character, sought to explain elasticity in terms of the constitution of the only example of a rubber then available, namely, natural (polyisoprene) rubber. It is significant that the proper understanding of the phenomenon owed much to the recognition of the very close connexion between natural rubber and many other materials, e.g. gelatin, muscle, silk, etc., of widely diverse

chemical composition. Symptomatic of this more general view-
point, there arose a realization of the possible significance of
thermal vibrations and rotations in long-chain molecules in
connexion with the problem of high elasticity. Such considerations represented a departure from the more usual idea of a
molecule as an essentially rigid structure whose form is determined by purely static forces. In 1931, for example, Haller
calculated the effect of thermal vibrations on a chain of the
paraffin type, represented as a planar zigzag (Haller, 1931).
The energy required to deform the valence angles and to stretch
the bond lengths was compared with the thermal energy of the
atoms, and it was shown that this thermal energy would lead
on the average to a considerable curvature. However, this
calculation ignored the much more important consideration of
rotations of the bonds.

The first exponents of the now generally accepted theory of
rubber elasticity were Meyer, von Susich, and Valko (1932) and
Karrer (1932, 1933), though the latter author was thinking
primarily of muscle. Meyer, von Susich, and Valko based their
theory on the consideration that the thermal energy of the
atoms of a long-chain molecule will lead to greater amplitudes
in the direction perpendicular to the chain than in the direction
of the chain, since the forces tending to restrict vibrations and
rotations in the lateral direction are much weaker than the
primary valence forces in the longitudinal direction. The effect
of this dissimilarity will be to produce a repulsive pressure
between parallel or extended chains, which repulsive pressure
will tend to draw the ends of the chains together and may thus
be regarded as equivalent to a longitudinal tension. Under the
influence of the lateral repulsive pressure the stretched rubber
will therefore retract 'until an irregular, statistically-determined
arrangement of the molecules and their parts is brought about,
in which condition molecular impacts no longer have a resultant
directional effect'. The quotation shows that Meyer, von
Susich, and Valko clearly appreciated the relation between
elasticity and the ability of the chain to take up an irregular
or statistically determined form by virtue of the interchange

of energy between its constituent elements and surrounding atoms. This is the fundamental concept of the now generally accepted theory of rubber elasticity.

The authors showed that their kinetic theory of elasticity led to the conclusion that the tension in a piece of stretched rubber should be directly proportional to the absolute temperature. This result they were able to confirm experimentally in work published at a later date.

Though using as an argument in favour of their theory the similarity in elastic properties exhibited by various materials (gelatin, cellulose, silk, etc.), Meyer, von Susich, and Valko appreciated the differences in degree of elasticity shown by different materials and drew attention to the significance of crystallization as a factor determining the range of elastic extensibility and other mechanical properties.

Karrer attempted to explain the properties of muscle on very similar lines and, like Meyer, von Susich, and Valko, regarded muscle as a member of a class of long-chain structures which included rubber. He noted that a long-chain molecule in which internal rotation about bonds can take place will be subject to Brownian motion at various portions of its structure, and will consequently take up a variously contorted shape unless restrained by a tensile force applied to its ends. This tendency of a chain to take up a random configuration was related to the principle of 'maximum mechanical chaos', or, as we should say in thermodynamic language, maximum entropy. In the normal or resting state the protein molecules in a muscle-fibre were assumed to be held in a parallel extended alinement by chemical forces; the process of retraction or activation of the muscle was then assumed to be initiated by chemical changes leading to the loosening of these intermolecular forces.

By thermodynamic reasoning, Karrer showed that the performance of work by the retracting muscle should be accompanied by an absorption of heat, or, in an adiabatic process, by a fall in temperature. The calculated amount of this fall, for the muscle in a frog's leg, was 0·006° C.

The kinetic theory has been greatly developed and elaborated in a quantitative sense by numerous workers since its original conception, and has been found to account so well for an increasing number of experimental observations that its position to-day is almost unchallenged. With all these developments, however, there has been no significant change in the fundamental physical basis of the theory, or in its principal thermodynamic consequences, which had been so clearly understood by Meyer and co-workers and by Karrer.

Nevertheless, the revolutionary character of the theory was in itself a hindrance to its ready acceptance, and many years elapsed before scientists generally were prepared to acknowledge its superiority over rival interpretations of rubber elasticity. To a certain extent this delay was due to a very proper scepticism with respect to a subject which had become over-burdened with a diversity of theories often of a highly speculative nature and with exceedingly little quantitative experimental data against which they could be critically examined.

The recent development of a wide range of synthetic rubbers has substantiated in a very convincing manner the fundamental assumption of the kinetic theory that elasticity is an attribute of a certain general type of molecular structure rather than of the specific constitution of the polyisoprene chain. A long-chain structure possessing internal flexibility by virtue of rotations about single bonds is a common feature of all rubbers, whether natural or synthetic.

We shall return to a more careful consideration of the elastic properties of long-chain molecules in the next chapter, and shall devote the remainder of the present chapter to a discussion of the general conditions for elasticity and the relation between the rubber-like state and other states of matter.

## 5. General conditions for elasticity

A very thorough analysis of the general conditions necessary for the appearance of rubber-like elasticity was carried out by Busse (1932). Though unaware at the time of the fundamental nature of the elasticity of the molecule, as revealed by Meyer, von Susich, and Valko, and by Karrer, Busse nevertheless arrived at a number of important conclusions relating to the nature of the forces between the molecules of an elastic medium and to its general structural pattern. The following discussion is based largely on Busse's work, modified only by the introduction of a detailed mechanism to account for the molecular elasticity.

As we have seen, the phenomenon of rubber like elasticity is associated with the so-called micro-Brownian motion of the individual elements of long-chain molecules. This type of motion is similar to the thermal motion of molecules of an ordinary liquid, with the single difference that the moving units, instead of being entirely independent, are connected together in the form of a chain. In certain respects, therefore, we should expect to find a very close similarity between the properties of rubbers and of liquids. This similarity is well shown by the X-ray diffraction pattern of an unstretched rubber, which is of the type corresponding to an amorphous or liquid structure, by the ability of unvulcanized natural rubber to dissolve in all proportions in suitable solvents, and by the fact that the deformation of rubber takes place substantially without change in volume, like the flow of a liquid. We may infer from these properties that the forces exerted by one molecule on another (referred to as *secondary* forces to distinguish them from the primary forces holding the atoms in the chain) are of the same order of magnitude as the intermolecular forces in an ordinary low-molecular liquid. Indeed the intermolecular forces in a liquid such as dihydromyrcene, comprising two isoprene units in a chain, cannot differ much from the intermolecular forces in polyisoprene rubber. These low intermolecular forces are indeed essential if the random rotations and the resulting changes in configuration of the molecules upon which their elasticity depends are to take place.

What, then, distinguishes a rubber from a liquid? If the intermolecular forces are low, as in a liquid, what is to prevent flow taking place by the free movement of each molecule over surrounding molecules?

A satisfactory answer to these questions can only be found

by introducing some form of restraint on the freedom of movement of the molecules. A suitable restraint, which does not
appreciably interfere with the necessary micro-Brownian motion
of the chain elements, may be obtained by introducing chemical
cross-links or points of junction between the chains at a very
few points along their length, so as to produce a three-dimensional network of interconnected chains. It is only by such
means that the contradictory requirements of freedom of
motion of chain elements and resistance to flow of the bulk
material can be simultaneously satisfied.

Summarizing the above conclusions, we may write down
the following three necessary conditions for the occurrence of
rubber-like elasticity.

1. The presence of long-chain molecules, possessing freely
   rotating links.
2. Weak secondary forces between the molecules.
3. An interlocking of the molecules at a few places along
   their length to form a three-dimensional network.

## 6. Vulcanization

The necessary cross-linkages between molecules are normally
introduced in the process of vulcanization. They are due to a
chemical reaction between the rubber and sulphur and are
comparable in strength with the primary bonds in the chain
itself. It is an essential requirement in rubber technology that
some form of vulcanization should be possible. Rubber articles
are extruded or moulded into their required form while the
rubber is in a semi-liquid or plastic condition; the final form
is then fixed and the required elasticity or rigidity secured by
vulcanization. In natural rubber the vulcanization reaction is
possible because of the highly reactive double bonds in the
polyisoprene chain. In synthetic rubbers the finding of a suitable cross-linking reaction may be a source of difficulty. Thus
the fully saturated polyisobutylene molecule (Table I), which
forms the basis of butyl rubber, cannot be vulcanized with
sulphur, and it is necessary to incorporate a small proportion
of an unsaturated compound, like isoprene or butadiene, into

the polymer chain in order to produce a technically valuable product which can be vulcanized.

Raw or unvulcanized rubber has, however, a considerable degree of elasticity, and it is only when it is subjected to prolonged stressing that flow becomes considerable. At first sight this fact would appear to stand in contradiction to the postulated necessity for cross-linkages, since raw rubber, being almost completely soluble in a suitable solvent, cannot therefore have the form of a chemically cross-linked network. The difficulty can be met only by assuming that in raw rubber the secondary or van der Waals' forces between chains may be sufficiently strong locally to produce effective cross-linkages of a physical rather than a chemical character. The effectiveness of these secondary forces will be greatly increased by the complex entanglements existing between the very long randomly-kinked chains. It is reasonable to suppose that the strength or permanence of these 'entanglement-cohesions' will vary greatly from one to another, and that the strongest of them will be broken down only by very prolonged stressing or by solvent action.

It is consistent with this point of view that the resistance to permanent or plastic deformation falls rapidly as the length of the chains is decreased. Raw rubber, in its natural state, has insufficient fluidity for such processes as moulding or extrusion; it is therefore first subjected to milling, or mastication, by which the molecular weight is reduced by thermal or oxidative breakdown of the chains, and is thus reduced to a 'soft' or plastic condition. The reduction in chain length or molecular weight varies, of course, with the degree of milling; for a typical compound the molecular weight in the final state might be about half that of the original material, that is to say, between 150,000 and 200,000.

## 7. The glassy state

The rubber-like state, as we have seen, depends on the possibility of random thermal motion of chain elements by rotation about single bonds. In any real material such rotation cannot be completely free from restrictions imposed by the presence of neighbouring groups of atoms either in the same molecule or in neighbouring molecules. The freedom of rotation will be a function of the relative values of the thermal energy of the rotating group and the potential barrier which has to be overcome in order that rotation may occur. The potential barrier will be only slightly dependent on temperature, whereas the average thermal energy increases with increasing temperature. The probability that a given group will surmount a potential barrier will be governed by a Boltzmann factor of the type $e^{-\epsilon/kT}$, and will therefore increase exponentially with temperature. This rapid temperature variation leads to the result that at low temperatures rotation will not take place at an appreciable rate. In this state the rubber no longer possesses rubber-like elasticity—it is hard and rigid like a glass.

The transition from the rubber-like to the glassy state at low temperatures is a phenomenon which is encountered in all rubbers, whether vulcanized or unvulcanized. The transition temperature naturally depends on the chemical constitution of the molecule. In unvulcanized natural rubber the transition occurs at about $-70°$ C. Vulcanization raises this temperature by 10 or 15 degrees, the exact amount depending on the manner and degree of vulcanization. The structure of the rubber is not affected by the transformation, the X-ray diffraction pattern, for example, being still the same as in the rubbery region. But many physical properties, such as thermal expansivity, specific heat, and thermal conductivity, undergo marked changes in the neighbourhood of the transition temperature. Transitions in some respects comparable with the transition to the glassy state in rubbers are found also in certain crystalline compounds and in organic glasses. Since they involve changes not in volume, heat content, or other *extensive properties*, but only in the rates of change with temperature of these properties, i.e. the so-called *intensive properties*, they are usually referred to as *second-order transitions*. An example of the variation of a particular quantity, in this case specific volume, on passing through the transition temperature, will be found in Fig. 9.2.

It is clear that any agency which increases the intermolecular forces will tend to raise the temperature of the second-order transition, whilst any agency tending to reduce these forces will have the converse effect. We should therefore expect polar or other strongly attractive side groups attached to the main chain to give a rubber with a high transition temperature. It is not, of course, possible to alter the intermolecular forces without at the same time introducing variations in other significant factors, such as closeness of packing, etc., but the evidence reveals the expected general trend. Thus, for example, the general-purpose synthetic rubber GR-S, which is an interpolymer of butadiene and styrene, has a higher transition temperature ($-61°$ C.) than polybutadiene ($\sim -75°$ C.) on account of the strong intermolecular force constant for the benzene rings in styrene. The transition temperature rises continuously with increasing proportions of styrene, while for pure polystyrene it is as high as $81°$ C. This material is a typical organic glass at ordinary temperatures, but exhibits rubber-like elasticity when heated above its transition temperature. The converse effect—reduction of transition temperature—is frequently achieved by the incorporation of a 'plasticizer' or low-molecular material whose function is to separate the polymer chains and thus to reduce intermolecular cohesion. A familiar example is polyvinyl chloride, with a transition temperature of $\sim 75°$ C., which acquires a degree of rubber-like elasticity by the addition of an ester such as tricresyl phosphate.

## 8. Crystallization

To complete this preliminary survey of the general properties of rubbers, reference must be made to the phenomenon of crystallization and its relation to molecular structure. The treatment in this section is of an introductory character, sufficient only to indicate its bearing on the problem of elasticity. The more detailed discussion of the subject will be deferred to a later chapter.

Crystallization may take two distinct forms. The first type of crystallization is produced by the freezing of unstretched rubber, whether vulcanized or unvulcanized. The axes of the crystallites are oriented randomly in all directions, and the X-ray diffraction pattern of such a frozen rubber is similar to that given by a crystalline powder. The second type of crystallization is that obtained by stretching rubber at ordinary temperatures; in this case the crystallites have one axis parallel to the direction of the extension, and give an X-ray pattern of discrete spots superposed on an 'amorphous' background. A pattern of this type, in which one axis only is oriented, is characteristic of natural fibres and oriented crystalline polymers generally, and is known as a 'fibre' diagram.

Unlike the second-order transition, crystallization is a process involving a definite structural change, or change of state, which is accompanied by the usual manifestations—latent heat of crystallization, change of specific volume, etc. Being a structural change it takes time. This time varies enormously according to the conditions under which crystallization takes place; it varies from a period of weeks or months for unstretched rubber to a small fraction of a second for a highly extended rubber, but the process is never instantaneous. For convenience we have distinguished crystallization by freezing from crystallization by stretching, but a closer study, in which extensions ranging from zero to 800 per cent. or more were applied, has revealed a continuous gradation from the one state to the other. In fact, crystallization by stretching differs from crystallization by freezing only in the fact of orientation and in the greater rapidity of the process.

Crystallization in rubbers is a more complex phenomenon than crystallization in ordinary low-molecular liquids, owing to the great length of the molecules. We are forced to assume that crystallization in rubbers takes place by local rearrangements of portions of molecules rather than by bulk movement of molecules, as in a liquid. Moreover, the dimensions of the crystallites have been estimated from the size of the X-ray diffraction spots to be only of the order of 100 to 1,000 Angstroms; the length of the molecules, on the other hand, averages (in natural rubber) about 20,000 Angstroms. From these and other considerations we are led to visualize a structure in crystalline rubbers of the kind shown diagrammatically in Fig. 1.3, in which a single molecule may pass alternately through a number of crystalline and amorphous regions. Because of the local intermolecular entanglements there must always remain some portions of the chains which cannot be fitted into a regular lattice. For this reason crystallization in rubbers cannot be complete; there must always be an appreciable fraction of uncrystallized or amorphous material.

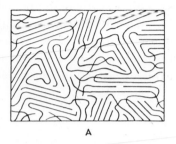

A

Much of the heat developed on stretching rubber is associated with the latent heat of crystallization. On account of this and a number of other striking effects connected with the phenomenon, it is not surprising to find that many of the early attempts to explain the elasticity of rubber were inclined to attribute to crystallization a predominant role in determining elastic properties. We know now that crystallization, although modifying the elastic behaviour of rubber, is not in itself an essential factor,

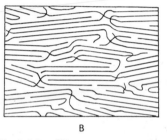

B

Fig. 1.3. Diagram representing the molecular structure of crystalline rubber (A) unstretched and (B) stretched before crystallizing. The parallel bundles represent crystallites.

but is to be regarded rather as a secondary or disturbing phenomenon. A conclusive demonstration of the validity of this deduction is provided by the development of a number of synthetic rubbers (butadiene-styrene and interpolymers generally) which, because of their structural irregularity, cannot be induced to crystallize under any conditions.

Crystalline frozen rubber, although harder than amorphous rubber, does not have the extreme hardness and associated brittleness of rubber in the glassy state. On account of the still flexible or amorphous segments of molecular chains binding the

4980.3　　　　　　　　　C

crystallites together, it is neither brittle like a glass nor plastic like a normal polycrystalline material, but retains a certain degree of flexibility or rubber-like elasticity, combined with toughness or resistance to fracture. An interesting example of a crystalline rubber is polyethylene (Table I) which, being crystalline at room temperature, is sufficiently rigid to maintain its shape even without vulcanization. This combination of mechanical properties with exceptionally high dielectric characteristics makes it an ideal material for use in high-frequency cables, where a limited degree of elasticity is all that is required.

# CHAPTER II

# INTERNAL ENERGY AND ENTROPY CHANGES ON DEFORMATION

## 1. Fundamental principles

FROM the point of view of the theoretical interpretation of the elasticity of rubber, the variation of elastic tension with changes in temperature is a matter of fundamental importance, as was indeed realized by Meyer when the kinetic theory of elasticity was first proposed. For if rubber elasticity is associated primarily with changes in entropy, the stress-temperature relations for rubbers should be entirely different from those applying to an ordinary hard solid, in which the elasticity is primarily related to changes in the internal energy of the material.

These expectations are borne out by the early experiments of Meyer and Ferri (1935), as is clearly shown by Fig. 2.1, taken from their paper, which represents the variation of tension with temperature, for a specimen of vulcanized rubber maintained at constant length. In order to obtain reproducible data it was found necessary to carry out a preliminary relaxation of the rubber at the highest temperature used at each particular extension. It is seen that at the higher extensions the tension increases with rising temperature while at lower extensions it decreases.

To understand the meaning of these phenomena, and the information obtainable from their quantitative study, it is necessary to consider the basic thermodynamic relations between force, length, and temperature on the one hand, and the thermodynamic quantities, internal energy and entropy, on the other. The fundamental relations which we require follow directly from the laws of thermodynamics. The first law provides us with a definition of internal energy, namely

$$dE = dQ + dW. \tag{2.1}$$

This equation states that the increase in internal energy $dE$ in any change taking place in a system is equal to the sum of the heat added to it $dQ$ and the work performed on it $dW$. The second law defines the entropy change $dS$ in any reversible process by the relation

$$T\,dS = dQ, \tag{2.2}$$

and hence, from (2.1), we have, for a reversible process,

$$dE = T\,dS + dW. \tag{2.3}$$

The argument which follows relates only to *reversible* or *equilibrium phenomena*, that is, to processes in which the state

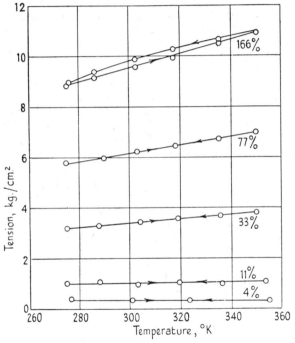

FIG. 2.1. Force at constant length as function of absolute temperature. Elongations as indicated. (Meyer and Ferri, 1935.)

of the system is precisely defined in terms of specified parameters, such as, for example, length and temperature. In discussing the equilibrium of such a system, it is convenient to introduce the *Helmholtz free energy* $A$, which is defined by the relation

$$A = E - TS. \tag{2.4}$$

For a change taking place *at constant temperature*, we have then

$$dA = dE - T\,dS. \tag{2.5}$$

Combining this result with (2.3), we have

$$dA = dW, \tag{2.6}$$

showing that the change in Helmholtz free energy in an isothermal change is equal to the work done on the system by the external forces.

In most thermodynamic text-books the subject is subsequently developed with particular reference to gases and liquids, in which the significant variables include pressure $P$ and volume $V$. The work done on the system in a small displacement is then written as

$$dW = -P\,dV.$$

In discussing problems related to the elasticity of solids, on the other hand, we are concerned primarily with the work done by the stress. If this is represented by a tensile force $f$, and $l$ is the length, measured in the direction of the force, the work done by the force in a displacement $dl$ is

$$dW = f\,dl. \tag{2.7}$$

When a hydrostatic pressure is acting in addition to the tensile stress, the total work performed is therefore

$$dW = f\,dl - P\,dV. \tag{2.7\,a}$$

For strict accuracy it is necessary to take account of both terms on the right-hand side of (2.7 a). But in the case of rubbers the volume change $dV$ is very small and if $P$ is the atmospheric pressure, the term $P\,dV$ is less than $f\,dl$ by a factor of $10^{-3}$ or $10^{-4}$. We may therefore neglect this term and use equation (2.7), which is accurate only at zero applied pressure or under constant volume conditions, in place of the complete expression (2.7 a).[†] By making use of equations (2.6) and (2.7) the tension may then be expressed in the form

$$f = (\partial W/\partial l)_T = (\partial A/\partial l)_T, \tag{2.8}$$

[†] Though volume changes may be neglected in relation to the external work $P\,dv$, it does not follow that they may be neglected in relation to the internal energy (cf. p. 30).

which shows that the *tension is equal to the change in Helmholtz free energy per unit extension.*

The significance of the important relation (2.8) may be better appreciated by reference to the accompanying Fig. 2.2, which represents diagrammatically the variation of Helmholtz free

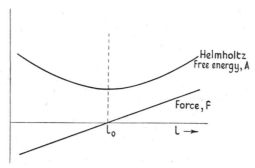

FIG. 2.2. Dependence of Helmholtz free energy and force on length. $l_0$ = unstrained length.

energy of an elastic body as a function of its length $l$. The normal unstressed state is that for which the free energy is a minimum, so that $(\partial A/\partial l)_T = 0$ at $l = l_0$. If $l$ is greater than $l_0$, $(\partial A/\partial l)_T$ is positive, corresponding to a tensile force, while if $l$ is less than $l_0$, $(\partial A/\partial l)_T$ is negative, corresponding to a compressive force.

For small strains, we may write

$$f = \left(\frac{\partial A}{\partial l}\right)_T = \left(\frac{\partial^2 A}{\partial l^2}\right)_T (l-l_0), \qquad (2.8\,a)$$

which means that the force may be considered to be a linear function of the deformation, with a constant of proportionality (Young's modulus), determined by the curvature of the free-energy curve. For large deformations, such as those encountered in rubber, the force-deformation curve will not, in general, be linear.

The tension, like the free energy, may be expressed as the sum of the two terms (from eqn. 2.5), thus,

$$f = (\partial E/\partial l)_T - T(\partial S/\partial l)_T, \qquad (2.9)$$

of which the first represents the change in internal energy with extension, and the second the change in entropy. This second term is related to the temperature coefficient of tension, as will now be shown.

Writing equation (2.4) in differential form, we have for any change (i.e. not necessarily isothermal)

$$dA = dE - T\, dS - S\, dT,$$

whilst from (2.3) and (2.7)

$$dE = f\, dl + T\, dS.$$

Combination of these two equations gives

$$dA = f\, dl - S\, dT.$$

Hence, by partial differentiation,

$$(\partial A/\partial l)_T = f \qquad \text{(cf. eqn. 2.8)}$$

and

$$(\partial A/\partial T)_l = -S. \qquad (2.10)$$

By a well-known property of partial differentials

$$\frac{\partial}{\partial l}\left(\frac{\partial A}{\partial T}\right)_l = \frac{\partial}{\partial T}\left(\frac{\partial A}{\partial l}\right)_T$$

and hence, from eqns. (2.10)

$$(\partial S/\partial l)_T = -(\partial f/\partial T)_l. \qquad (2.11)$$

Equation (2.11) gives the entropy change per unit extension in terms of a measurable quantity $(\partial f/\partial T)_l$, the temperature coefficient of tension. Insertion of this relation in (2.9) gives for the corresponding internal energy change

$$(\partial E/\partial l)_T = f - T(\partial f/\partial T)_l. \qquad (2.12)$$

The relations (2.11) and (2.12) are of fundamental importance in rubber elasticity, since they provide a direct means of determining experimentally both the internal energy and entropy changes accompanying a deformation. The only experimental data which it is necessary to provide for this purpose are a set of equilibrium values of the tension at constant length over a range of temperature. If, for example, the curve $CC'$ in Fig. 2.3 represents the variation with temperature of the force at constant length, its slope at the point $P$, which is $(\partial f/\partial T)_l$, is, by equation (2.11), equal to the entropy change per unit extension $(\partial S/\partial l)_T$ when the rubber is extended isothermally at the temperature $T$. In a corresponding way, the intercept $OA$ of the tangent to the curve at $P$ on the vertical axis $T = 0$ (absolute zero), is $f - T(\partial f/\partial T)_l$, which by equation (2.12) is equal to the internal energy change per unit extension $(\partial E/\partial l)_T$.

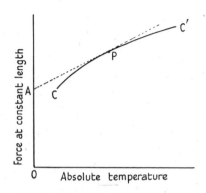

Fig. 2.3. Slope and intercept of stress-temperature curve.

The course of the internal energy and entropy changes accompanying the deformation may thus be obtained by direct inspection of the stress-temperature curves. In particular, if these curves are linear (as in Meyer and Ferri's data, Fig. 2.1) both internal energy and entropy terms are independent of temperature. If, in addition, the stress-temperature relation is represented by a straight line passing through the origin, the internal energy term is zero. It follows that in this case the elastic force arises solely from the change in entropy.

## 2. Experimental investigations

Although in principle the determination of the internal energy and entropy contributions to the force of extension is simple, the practical carrying out of the necessary operations is not entirely straightforward. The reason for this is that rubber— even when vulcanized in the most suitable manner—is by no means an ideally elastic material, so that, for a given temperature and extension, there is not a single unequivocally determinable value of the stress. Instead the stress is subject to various irreversible changes with time, which must somehow be eliminated or suppressed, if equilibrium values (which alone are susceptible to thermodynamic analysis) are to be attained.

### The early work of Meyer and Ferri

As stated in § 1, Meyer and Ferri carried out a preliminary relaxation of the rubber at a high temperature at each value of the extension. With this precaution they were able to obtain substantially reversible stress-temperature curves, over a con-

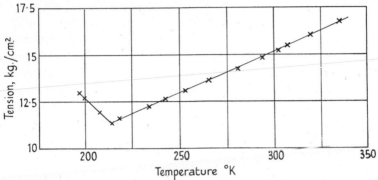

Fig. 2.4. Force at constant length as function of absolute temperature. Extension, 350 per cent. (Meyer and Ferri, 1935.)

siderable range of temperature and elongation, provided that the extension was not high enough to cause crystallization. A typical curve, representing the behaviour of a rubber vulcanized with 8 per cent. of sulphur, is illustrated in Fig. 2.4. The stress-temperature relation is linear over a very large range of temperature, i.e. from $-50°$ to $70°$ C. It is therefore concluded that the elastic tension is due almost entirely to the entropy term, in agreement with the prediction of the kinetic theory of elasticity. At $-50°$ C. the temperature coefficient of tension exhibits an abrupt reversal of sign. This corresponds to the transition to the glass-hard state, where the rubber loses its characteristic extensibility. The behaviour then corresponds to that of an ordinary hard solid, with the internal energy term dominant.

Coming as it did so early in the history of the kinetic theory,

Meyer and Ferri's experimental result, published in 1935, was of great importance in helping to establish the validity of the new interpretation. Though theirs was not the first investigation of the kind—the work of Wiegand and Snyder (1934) in particular had already pointed to a similar conclusion—it was the first to achieve a reasonably satisfactory approach to equilibrium values of the tension over a wide range of temperature.

### The experiments of Guth and co-workers.

More recent experiments, while confirming Meyer and Ferri's original conclusions in a general way, have concentrated particularly on the accurate derivation of the small but significant internal energy changes which accompany the extension. Among these, the investigations of Guth and co-workers on both natural and synthetic rubbers are of particular importance. The experimental technique employed in these studies was essentially similar to that used by Meyer and Ferri; at each particular length the specimen was allowed to relax at the highest temperature employed ($\sim 70°$ C.) until the rate of stress decay had become small compared with the time taken to carry out the experiment. Some of the data obtained by Anthony, Caston, and Guth (1942) in this way are represented in Fig. 2.5, which refers to a natural rubber vulcanized with 8 per cent. of sulphur (the same as that used by Meyer and Ferri). The stress-temperature curves at constant length are seen to be linear, and the points for rising and falling temperatures are in close agreement, this being taken as an indication that reversibility had been achieved. The reversal of the slope below about 10 per cent. extension, the so-called *thermo-elastic inversion point*, is evident here, as it was in Meyer and Ferri's data. Calculation of the terms $(\partial S/\partial l)_T$ and $(\partial E/\partial l)_T$ from these curves, by means of equations (2.11) and (2.12), yielded the result shown in Fig. 2.6. It is evident from this figure that the form of the force-elongation curve is effectively due to the entropy term $(\partial S/\partial l)_T$. Except at small extensions ($< 100$ per cent.) the internal energy term accounts for not more than one-sixth of the observed tension or free-energy change. At low extensions,

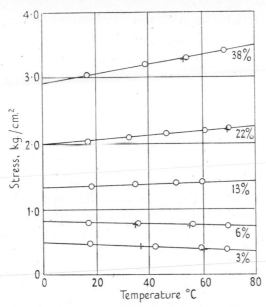

FIG. 2.5. Force at constant length as function of temperature. Elongations as indicated. (Anthony, Caston, and Guth, 1942.)

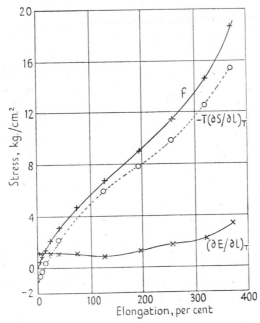

FIG. 2.6. Changes in internal energy ($E$) and entropy ($S$) accompanying extension of rubber. (Anthony, Caston, and Guth, 1942.)

however, the internal energy changes are of the same order of magnitude as the entropy term, while the latter, instead of remaining negative (as required by the kinetic theory), changes sign at an extension corresponding to the thermo-elastic inversion point.

## 3. The thermo-elastic inversion phenomenon

In § 1 attention was drawn to the observation by Meyer and Ferri (Fig. 2.1), later confirmed by Anthony, Caston, and Guth (Fig. 2.5), that whilst above about 10 per cent. elongation the tension at constant length increases with rising temperature, at lower elongation the variation with temperature is in the opposite direction.

Meyer and Ferri correctly interpreted this thermo-elastic inversion phenomenon in terms of the expansion of volume of the rubber on heating. This expansion will clearly have the effect of tending to increase the length at constant stress, which is equivalent to reducing the tension at constant length. At very low stresses the reduction of tension by thermal expansion exceeds the increase of tension to be expected from the kinetic theory of elasticity; the thermo-elastic inversion point is the elongation at which these two effects exactly balance. We shall see later that this explanation has been confirmed by Meyer's later experiments on rubber subjected to a shearing strain.

The fact that volume changes enter into the thermo-elastic phenomena of rubber in no way limits the applicability of the fundamental equations (2.11) and (2.12) for the derivation of the internal energy and entropy changes on extension. These relations are purely phenomenological; they do not imply any particular mechanism. It is in the interpretation—not in the derivation—of the internal energy and entropy changes that physical or molecular concepts may usefully be introduced. In this connexion, the explanation of the thermo-elastic inversion put forward by Meyer and Ferri is of the utmost significance since it points to the importance of hitherto neglected volume changes in the discussion of the thermodynamics of rubber elasticity.

## 4. Later experimental work

In later experimental work, notably by Wood and Roth (1944), Roth and Wood (1944), and Gee (1946), the question of the best conditions for the attainment of the desired equilibrium stresses has been more fully explored. Thus Wood and Roth found the observed stress to depend on the temperature

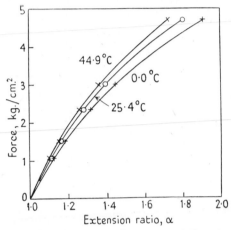

FIG. 2.7. Equilibrium force-extension curves at three temperatures.
(Gee, 1946.)

at which the initial relaxation was carried out; so long as the relaxation temperature was not exceeded, and provided that crystallization was avoided, they were able to obtain reproducible stress-temperature lines.

Gee's method was based on the observation that a rubber swollen with a solvent appears to be more perfectly elastic and suffers less from hysteresis and relaxation effects than a normal dry rubber. This is because the solvent breaks down the semi-permanent intermolecular cohesions, thus giving a more rapid approach to the equilibrium state. Gee therefore allowed his stretched specimen to imbibe petroleum vapour, which was subsequently removed by drying *in vacuo*. In this way he was able to obtain reproducible data, which probably represent a closer approach to true thermodynamic equilibrium than any previously recorded.

Gee found it convenient to consider the temperature variation of stress at constant extension ratio rather than at constant length. Fig. 2.7 represents the equilibrium force-elongation curves at three different temperatures, plotted against extension ratio $\alpha$, derived from the data given in his paper. The effect of plotting in this way is that the thermo-elastic inversion phenomenon disappears, and, as will be seen from an examination of Fig. 2.7, the tension at constant extension ratio is strictly proportional to the absolute temperature, at least up to about 100 per cent. elongation.

## 5. Further thermodynamic considerations

To understand the significance of Gee's result it is necessary to carry out a more refined thermodynamic analysis in which volume changes are taken into account. Such an analysis has been made by Elliott and Lippmann (1945) and by Gee (1946). It is only necessary here to refer to the principal conclusions to which the analysis leads.

The experiments are performed at constant pressure $P$, and it is required to derive the internal energy change on extension at constant pressure and temperature $(\partial E/\partial l)_{P,T}$ and the corresponding entropy change $(\partial S/\partial l)_{P,T}$ in terms of the measured temperature coefficient of tension at constant extension ratio $\alpha$, namely $(\partial f/\partial T)_{P,\alpha}$. The relation connecting these quantities (Gee, 1946) is

$$(\partial E/\partial l)_{P,T} = f - T(\partial f/\partial T)_{P,\alpha} + \beta l T(\partial f/\partial l)_{P,T}, \qquad (2.13)$$

where $\beta$ is the coefficient of linear expansion of the unstrained rubber,[†] and $(\partial f/\partial l)_{P,T}$ is the slope of the force-elongation curve. Since all the quantities on the right-hand side of (2.13) are known, the internal energy change may be evaluated. For the particular case of natural rubber, for extensions up to about 100 per cent., Gee's experiments yield the result that at constant $\alpha$, $f$ is proportional to $T$, i.e.

$$f - T(\partial f/\partial T)_{P,\alpha} = 0, \qquad (2.14)$$

---

[†] In equation (2.13) it is assumed that $E$ is not significantly different from the heat content $H$ $(= E + PV)$. This is certainly true when $P$ is the atmospheric pressure.

and therefore, from (2.13),

$$(\partial E/\partial l)_{P,T} = \beta l T (\partial f/\partial l)_{P,T}. \qquad (2.15)$$

The corresponding entropy change $(\partial S/\partial l)_{P,T}$ is readily obtained from the relation (cf. 2.9)

$$f = (\partial E/\partial l)_{P,T} - T(\partial S/\partial l)_{P,T}. \qquad (2.16)$$

The resultant internal energy and entropy changes obtained by

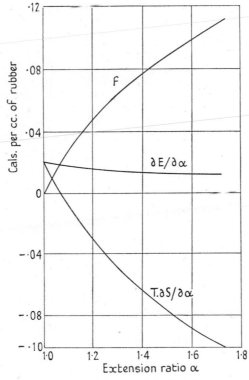

FIG. 2.8. Changes in internal energy ($E$) and entropy ($S$) accompanying extension of rubber. (Gee, 1946.)

Gee, using these thermodynamic formulae, are reproduced in Fig. 2.8.

The data obtained by Wood and Roth for natural rubber cover a larger range of extension. Fig. 2.9 represents their force-elongation curve and the value of $f - T(\partial f/\partial T)_{P,\alpha}$ which is approximately equivalent to the internal energy change at

constant volume. The latter is very small up to about 200 per
cent. elongation, then becomes increasingly negative as crystallization develops.

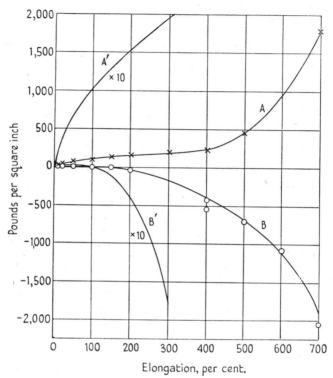

FIG. 2.9. Variation of stress (*A*) and stress-temperature intercept (*B*) with
elongation. The early parts of the curves are shown on a larger scale (*A'*, *B'*).
(Wood and Roth, 1944.)

## 6. The significance of volume changes

Up to this point the conclusions derived by Gee, and represented in Fig. 2.8, do not appear to differ significantly from
the earlier results of Guth and his co-workers, illustrated by
Fig. 2.6, which were based on an equally valid and strictly
accurate method of analysis. The real significance of the more
refined treatment appears, however, when an attempt is made
to interpret these experimental data. This may be seen by
considering the approximate expression given by Gee (1946)

for the internal energy change under constant volume conditions, i.e.

$$(\partial E/\partial l)_{V,T} \simeq f - T(\partial f/\partial T)_{P,\alpha}. \tag{2.17}$$

Now, as we have already seen, Gee's experimental conclusion is that the quantity on the right-hand side of (2.17) is zero, at least up to 100 per cent. extension. It follows, therefore, that *for an extension carried out at constant volume the internal energy change is zero*. The obvious further deduction to be drawn from this conclusion is that the internal energy changes observed when rubber is extended in the usual way (i.e. at constant pressure) are associated directly with changes in volume. From the physical standpoint this means that these internal energy changes arise from the changes in interatomic distances which accompany the application of the stress.

Further calculations by Gee lend support to this deduction. On the assumption that the internal energy changes are due solely to the associated volume changes, it should be possible to calculate from them the corresponding changes in volume. The appropriate relationship involves the compressibility and the thermal expansion coefficient, both of which are known. Using Wood and Roth's data Fig. (2.9) Gee calculated in this way the volume changes shown in Fig. 2.10. For comparison the changes of volume on stretching obtained by the direct measurements of Holt and McPherson (1934) are also shown.

These volume changes arise from two causes. First, at low extensions, there is a small increase of volume, amounting at most to 0·1 per cent. This expansion, which has not yet been measured directly with any precision, arises, as Gee was able to show, from the hydrostatic component of the applied tension and is entirely similar to the expansion which a liquid would undergo if subjected to a negative hydrostatic pressure. The very much larger contraction of volume which occurs at extensions exceeding 300 per cent. is undoubtedly due to crystallization.

*Meyer's experiments on shear*

Finally, as a further illustration of the significance of volume changes in determining the internal energy changes which are observed when rubber is subjected to extension, mention may be made of the experiments of Meyer and van der Wyk (1946) which were concerned with a shear strain. The rubber sample was contained in the annular space between two coaxial cylinders, and was sheared by rotation of the outer cylinder with respect to the inner. The special feature of this experiment is

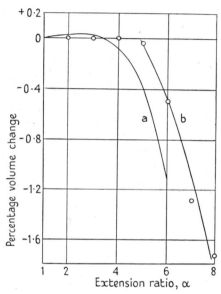

FIG. 2.10. Volume changes on extension. (a) Calculated from Roth and Wood. (b) Measured by Holt and McPherson.

that a shear is a type of strain involving no change of volume. If, as is believed, the internal energy changes are associated with volume changes, they may be expected to disappear under these conditions. Meyer and van der Wyk limited their observations to quite small strains, so that there was no question of complications due to crystallization. In this region they found that the stress was proportional to the temperature; there was no thermo-elastic inversion, and no internal energy change, within the limits of the experimental errors.

## 7. Recapitulation

Summing up the evidence presented in this first part of the chapter, it may be observed that in spite of the very considerable experimental difficulties involved in obtaining really reversible stress-temperature relations, there is already a substantial degree of agreement both on the experimental behaviour of rubber and on the theoretical interpretation of this behaviour. The picture which emerges confirms the basic postulate of the kinetic theory of elasticity, that the elasticity of a rubber, at least for not too large deformations, arises primarily from a change in entropy. In addition to the entropy changes there are internal energy changes, which are, however, of a secondary character and arise from the essentially *liquid* properties of the rubber. These internal energy changes do not contribute appreciably to the elastic stress. This conclusion is applicable to all rubbers at sufficiently small deformations. In the region of larger deformations specific differences are observable in the variations of internal energy with extension between various types of rubber; these differences almost certainly arise from secondary forces between partially alined molecules, leading to changes in local structure or, in the extreme case, to crystallization.

## 8. Thermal effects of extension

The fact that rubber becomes heated when stretched adiabatically has been known for a long time. The first observation of the phenomenon was reported by Gough (1805). Gough noticed also that a piece of rubber, extended by a constant load, contracted when the temperature was raised, which means that at constant length the tension increased with increasing temperature. Kelvin (1855) was probably the first to consider the thermodynamic implications of Gough's observations, and succeeded in showing that the positive stress-temperature coefficient was a necessary thermodynamic consequence of the evolution of heat on extension. He concluded that the tensile force must arise from the 'motion of the constituent particles' of the material. This remarkable deduction unfortunately came before its time, and appears to have been lost sight of for nearly eighty years.

By the second law of thermodynamics, as represented by equation (2.2), the evolution of heat $(-dQ)$ in a reversible change gives a direct measure of the change of entropy in the process. If heat is evolved on the extension of any material, the entropy change is negative. Conversely, if heat is absorbed, the entropy change is positive. If there is no internal energy change, the heat evolved in an isothermal deformation is, by equation (2.3), equal to the work done on the material, otherwise it is equal to the difference between the work done on the material and the change in its internal energy. On account of the smallness of the heat effects in rubber, it is usual to measure the change of temperature in an adiabatic deformation rather than the heat evolved in an isothermal deformation. Under adiabatic conditions, that is, under conditions in which the body neither gains nor loses heat, the entropy change is, by definition, zero, and the change in temperature is given by the relation (since $\delta T = \delta Q/c_l$)

$$(\partial T/\partial l)_S = -(1/c_l)(\partial Q/\partial l)_T, \qquad (2.18)$$

where $c_l$ is the specific heat at constant length, and $(\partial Q/\partial l)_T$ is the isothermal heat of extension.

This expression gives the change in temperature corresponding to an increase in length $dl$. The change in temperature in a quick extension from the initial length $l_0$ to the final length $l$ is obtained by integration of (2.18) with respect to $l$. In this way the temperature rise $\Delta T$ becomes

$$\Delta T = \frac{T}{c_l} \int_{l_0}^{l} (\partial S/\partial l)_T \, dl. \qquad (2.19)$$

A careful investigation of the temperature changes on extending vulcanized rubber was made by Joule (1859), who used a thermocouple in contact with the rubber for this purpose. His results, which are reproduced in Fig. (2.11), showed an initial cooling followed by a rapidly rising heating effect as the extension was increased.† In showing a predominant heating effect, these experiments confirmed the original observations of Gough, for which reason the phenomenon is usually referred to as the Gough–Joule effect.

† To convert these data into quantities of heat, $c_l$ in equation (2.18) may be taken as approximately 0·45 for vulcanized rubber.

An investigation of the heating effect in a natural rubber vulcanizate, based on the work of Dart, has more recently been reported by James and Guth (1943). A slight difference between the effects on extension and on retraction respectively was found, due to the irreversible phenomena of relaxation. The

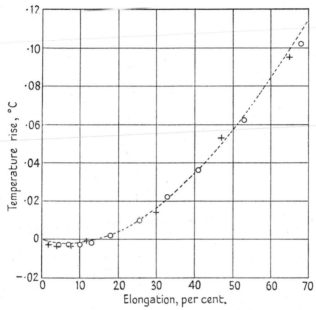

FIG. 2.11. Temperature rise in adiabatic extension. + Joule's experiments. o James and Guth's experiments. --- James and Guth, theoretical.

data reproduced in Fig. 2.11 are mean figures for extension and retraction. The general shape of the curve agrees with Joule's earlier result, as would be expected, though the quantitative agreement must be regarded as fortuitous, since the effect will depend on the degree of vulcanization (i.e. the modulus) of the rubber, data for which are not available.

The course of the thermal changes with increasing extension may be compared with the entropy data derived from stress-temperature measurements, as discussed in the preceding section. Thus, the initial cooling corresponds to the initial positive entropy of extension (Fig. 2.8), which, as we have seen, is associated with the expansivity of the rubber, while the subsequent heating corresponds to the large negative entropy term arising from the configuration of the molecular network. Fig. 2.11 includes for comparison the heat changes calculated by James and Guth (1943) from the internal energy and entropy

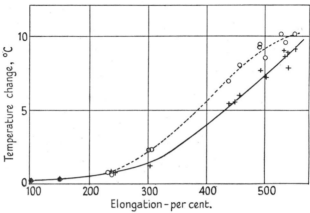

FIG. 2.12. Temperature change in adiabatic extension (or retraction).
—— Extension, --- Retraction. (Dart, Anthony, and Guth, 1942.)

changes derived from their theoretical network model, the parameters being adjusted to give the best fit between the theoretical and experimental entropy curves for the particular rubber investigated by Dart.

At higher elongations the variations in the heat effect, like the variations in internal energy discussed in the previous section, are more complex and depend noticeably on the type of rubber. This is brought out by the series of investigations by Dart, Anthony, and Guth (1942) on a number of natural and synthetic rubbers.

Typical data for a vulcanized latex rubber are shown in Fig. 2.12. Up to about 230 per cent. extension the curve is reversible. Beyond this point the heating increases rather sharply and is no longer reversible, the cooling on retraction being greater than the heating on extension. This very large thermal effect represents the latent heat of crystallization, which is superposed on the normal effect due to the change in configurational entropy. The higher effect on retraction is explained by the time-lag in the crystallization process which Dart, Anthony, and Guth were actually able to follow thermally. Comparable effects are found in other properties related to crystallization, for example, in the double refraction; these effects will be discussed in a later chapter. Neoprene (polychloroprene), which also crystallizes on stretching, shows a rather similar heat curve to that for natural rubber, but in this case the retraction curve falls below the extension curve. This is probably due to the increased importance of relaxation with this rubber.

Rubbers which do not crystallize do not show the very large heat of extension (up to 14° C.) of natural rubber and neoprene. This is illustrated by Hycar OH (butadiene-acrylic nitrile), in which the maximum heating is less than 2° C. An 8 per cent. sulphur natural rubber vulcanizate also showed little if any crystallization, the maximum temperature rise being only 3° C. This confirms the evidence presented by Meyer and Ferri (1935) for such a compound.

While thermal measurements are less accurate than stress-temperature measurements for the purpose of calculating the internal energy and entropy changes on extension, the results reported here undoubtedly serve to enlarge our understanding of the thermodynamic behaviour of rubber. So far as they go these results are consistent with the conclusions arrived at from the study of the stress-temperature relations. They prove in a very direct manner one necessary consequence of the kinetic theory of elasticity, that *the process of deformation of rubber involves a reversible transformation of work into heat.* Taken as a whole, these thermodynamic investigations have laid a sure foundation for the detailed statistical development of the kinetic theory, which will be the subject of the following chapters, while at the same time they provide valuable information on its necessary limitations and on the degree of validity of its main assumptions.

# CHAPTER III

# THE ELASTICITY OF LONG-CHAIN MOLECULES

## 1. Statistical properties of long-chain molecules

THE development of the theory of rubber elasticity on the basis of the structural and thermodynamic concepts outlined in the preceding chapters may be thought of as taking place in two stages. In the first stage the statistical properties of the single long-chain molecule are treated in a quantitative manner, leading to mathematical expressions for the probability and entropy of the chain as a function of the distance between its ends, and hence to a more complete description of the elasticity of the molecule. The second stage consists in the treatment of a network of such long-chain molecules by statistical methods, whereby the mechanical properties of the bulk material may be quantitatively represented. The present chapter is concerned with the first of these problems—the statistical treatment of the single long-chain molecule—while the development of the network theory will be the subject of the one which follows.

The statistical treatment of the single molecule is a somewhat difficult problem to solve accurately. Indeed, a complete solution which could be regarded as representing exactly the properties of any real molecular structure has not been obtained. The various attempted solutions necessarily involve the representation of the actual molecule by a more or less idealized mathematical abstraction, in which for the sake of simplicity certain physically significant aspects of the problem are ignored. In addition, the treatment of the idealized model may be carried to various stages of approximation. The present discussion will be limited to the first approximation, which is sufficient for the description of most of the essential properties of rubber, provided that the strains are not excessively large. The higher approximations, applicable for all values of the strain, will be dealt with at a later stage (Chapter VI).

*The paraffin chain*

The problem of the calculation of the statistical properties of a long-chain molecule is essentially of the same kind whatever the detailed structure of the chain. By way of illustration we may take the simplest possible chain structure, namely the

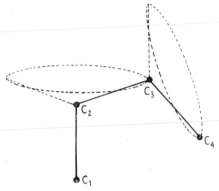

Fig. 3.1. Rotations about bonds in paraffin molecule.

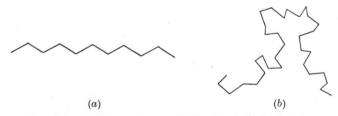

(a)                                    (b)

Fig. 3.2. (a) Planar zigzag. (b) Randomly kinked chain.

paraffin or polyethylene molecule $(CH_2)_n$. It is assumed that each C—C bond permits of free rotation, so that, for example, the bond $C_2C_3$ (Fig. 3.1) may be considered to rotate about $C_1C_2$ as axis, while $C_3C_4$ rotates about $C_2C_3$ as axis, and so on. Under these conditions, if the number of bonds is large, the chain will, in general, assume an irregularly kinked form, as in Fig. 3.2 (b), rather than the straightened or planar zigzag form of 3.2 (a). The actual configuration will be subject to continual fluctuation, since the bond rotations are of a random thermal character. We cannot, of course, define the precise form of the molecule, but we may hope to specify some of its statistical properties, and in particular the following:

(a) the root-mean-square value of $r$, the distance between the ends of the chain, and

(b) the probability of any given distance $r$ between the ends.

For the paraffin chain, Eyring (1932) has derived an expression for the mean square value of $r$ in terms of the number of links in the chain $n$, the length of the link $l$, and the semi-angle $\alpha$ of the cone of rotation. His result is

$$r^2 = l^2[n + 2(n-1)\cos\alpha + 2(n-2)\cos^2\alpha + \ldots + 2\cos^{n-1}\alpha]. \quad (3.1)$$

If $n$ is large, this expression reduces to the simpler form

$$\overline{r^2} = nl^2 \frac{1+\cos\alpha}{1-\cos\alpha}, \quad (3.1\,a)$$

showing that, for a long chain, the *root-mean-square value of $r$, the distance between ends, is proportional to the square root* of the number of links. For the paraffin chain the valence angle is $109\frac{1}{2}°$, giving $\alpha = 70\frac{1}{2}°$, and therefore $\cos\alpha = 1/3$, so that

$$\sqrt{(\overline{r^2})} = l\sqrt{(2n)}. \quad (3.1\,b)$$

As an aid to the better appreciation of the form of the statistically kinked chain, the author has constructed a wire model to represent a paraffin molecule of 1,000 links (Fig. 3.2 (c)). In the construction of this model the links were set at the required valence angle, while the angular position of each link in the circle of rotation was selected in a random manner by the throw of a die. This gave the choice of six equally spaced positions of rotation—a sufficiently close approximation to complete randomness. The form obtained was of course only one of many possible forms which might have been chosen, but it happened to be a fairly 'average' sample; the end-to-end distance, for example, was very near to the theoretically most probable length.

*Polyisoprene chains*

The calculation of the mean square length of a molecule is not limited to the case where all the bonds and valence angles are equal. A method of treating more complicated structures has been worked out by Wall (1943 a) and applied to the case of the polyisoprene chain (Fig. 1.2), in which there is one double bond for each group of three single bonds. The two single bonds adjoining the double bond do not rotate but are in a fixed

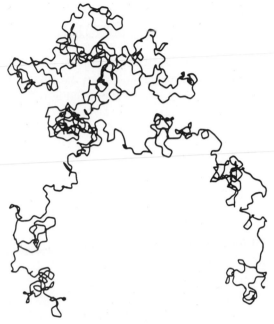

FIG. 3.2. (c) Form of 1,000-link paraffin chain according to the statistical theory.

plane. Wall considered both natural rubber, in which the single bonds have the *cis*-configuration with respect to the double bonds, and gutta-percha, which is otherwise similar to natural rubber, but in which the *trans*-arrangement occurs. He considered also the case of a random mixture of *cis* and *trans* elements in the chain. His somewhat lengthy formulae will not be written out in full; it will be sufficient here to quote the numerical results obtained when the usual values of bond lengths and valence angles are inserted. For the *cis*-arrangement (natural rubber) the result is, for a sufficiently large value of $n$, the total number of bonds,

$$\sqrt{(\overline{r^2})} = 2{\cdot}01\sqrt{n} \quad \text{Angstrom units,} \qquad (3.2\,a)$$

while for the *trans*-arrangement (gutta-percha)

$$\sqrt{(\overline{r^2})} = 2 \cdot 90\sqrt{n} \quad \text{Angstrom units.} \tag{3.2 b}$$

Thus for a given chain length the average end-to-end distance is greater for the *trans*- than for the *cis*-configuration.

As Wall points out, this difference would lead to a greater potential elastic extensibility in natural rubber, compared with gutta-percha, for molecules of the same chain length (or molecular weight). The striking difference in the physical properties of the two materials cannot, however, be attributed to this comparatively small difference in potential extensibility, but is due rather to the fact that gutta-percha is highly crystalline at ordinary temperatures, while natural rubber exists normally in the amorphous state.

## 2. Hindered rotation

These calculations of the root-mean-square lengths of molecules, while correctly introducing the valence angle condition, neglect any possible steric hindrances to rotation. They assume that all positions of the rotating bond are equally probable. This assumption of completely free rotation is a convenient approximation, but does not correspond exactly to the conditions in an actual molecular chain, where forces of attraction and repulsion between neighbouring atoms attached to the chain are likely to play a significant part, so that certain positions of rotation may be more probable than other positions. Such effects are known to exist, and have been examined experimentally in a number of molecules. Thus, for example, in ethane ($CH_3$—$CH_3$), studies by Pitzer (1937) and by Kistiakowsky, Lacher, and Stitt (1939) on the specific heat (which is related to the number of degrees of freedom) have revealed the presence of an energy barrier of 3,000 calories per mole separating the most favoured positions of rotation about the C—C bond, while a similar study of propane ($CH_3$—$CH_2$—$CH_3$) indicated a potential barrier of about the same amount (3,300 cals./mole) restricting the rotation of the methyl groups (Kemp and Egan, 1938). An energy barrier of this magnitude (i.e. $\sim 5kT$), while not preventing rotation, leads to different probabilities for different positions of rotation, and thus invalidates the simple statistical treatment based on completely free rotation.

The existence of an energy barrier in ethane and propane is due to the repulsive forces between hydrogen atoms, arising from the fact that in the less favourable positions hydrogen atoms are brought to within a smaller distance from each

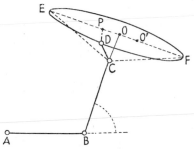

Fɪɢ. 3.3. Illustrating hindered rotation.

other than that corresponding to their normal 'van der Waals' separation. This mutual interference of hydrogen atoms may be reduced, for example, by the removal of some of the hydrogen atoms, that is to say, by the substitution of a double or triple bond for a single bond. Thus in dimethyl acetylene

$$(CH_3—C≡C—CH_3)$$

the energy barrier restricting rotation of the terminal methyl groups is found to be not more than 500 cals./mole (Osborne, Garner, and Yost, 1940). In natural rubber, also, the presence of the double bond would be expected to increase the freedom of rotation about neighbouring single bonds.

The effect of internal restrictions on the statistical length of the chain will depend on the relative probabilities of the different positions of rotation. If, for example, in the paraffin-type chain the more extended *trans*-configuration is favoured compared with the more folded *cis*-form, the result will be to increase the average extension of the chain. The problem may be dealt with mathematically in general terms by postulating a potential function $V(\phi)$ to describe the variation of potential with the angle of rotation $\phi$ of a particular bond ($\widehat{DOP}$, Fig. 3.3).

The relative probability of the angle $\phi$ is then obtained by introducing a Boltzmann factor, i.e.

$$p(\phi)\,d\phi = Ce^{-V(\phi)/kT}\,d\phi. \tag{3.3}$$

To simplify the problem, let us suppose that the function $V(\phi)$ is symmetrical with respect to the plane $ABC$, and has maxima and minima at $E$ and $F$ respectively. Let $P$ be the

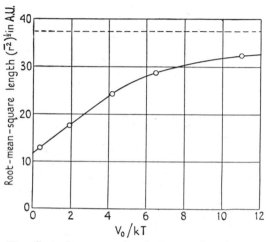

FIG. 3.4. The effect of an energy barrier to rotation ($V_0$) on the root-mean-square length of a 30-link paraffin chain. (Benoît, 1947.)

projection of the moving atom $D$ on the diameter $EF$, and let $O'$ be the mean position of $P$. For unrestricted rotation $O'$ would coincide with the centre $O$ of the circle of rotation; in the presence of the restrictive potential the distance $OO'$ gives a measure of the departure from randomness. If $OO'/OE$ is denoted by $a$, then

$$a = \int_{-\pi}^{\pi} p(\phi)\cos\phi\,d\phi. \tag{3.4}$$

The mean square length is a function of $a$, and is given by the formula (Sadron, 1946, Taylor, 1947, Benoît, 1947)

$$\overline{r^2} = nl^2\frac{1+\cos\alpha}{1-\cos\alpha}\,\frac{1+a}{1-a} \tag{3.5}$$

in which the symbols have the same connotation as in (3.1). Since $a$ involves the temperature, it follows that the mean square length is no longer independent of temperature when the rotation is restricted. At sufficiently high temperatures the parameter $a$ tends to zero, and (3.5) reduces to the Eyring formula (3.1 $a$).

Numerical calculations by Benoît give the root-mean-square length of a 30-link paraffin chain as a function of $V_0/kT$, where $V_0$ is the height of the energy barrier. His result (Fig. 3.4) shows that a value of $V_0/kT$ of only 1·0 (corresponding to an energy barrier of about 600 cals./mole) is sufficient to increase the root-mean-square length by 25 per cent., while for $V_0/kT = 4·0$ this length is approximately doubled.

## 3. The distribution of molecular lengths

This discussion of the average or root-mean-square end-to-end distance of a long-chain molecule shows that when the rotation about bonds is free, or only slightly hindered, the root-mean-square length is proportional to the square root of the number of bonds in the chain. Since the fully-extended chain length is proportional to the number of bonds, it follows that the potential elastic extensibility of the chain is also proportional to $n^{\frac{1}{2}}$, that is, to the square root of the chain length. This deduction shows immediately that the very high elastic extensibility found in rubbery materials can only be expected to occur if the chain length is sufficiently great, and therefore leads us to expect a general relation between molecular weight and degree of extensibility which is, in fact, borne out by observation.

For the more complete discussion of the elastic properties of long-chain molecules it is necessary to inquire into the distribution of $r$-values about the mean, or more generally, into the form of the distribution function expressed in terms of the components of the vector distance $r$ referred to fixed coordinate axes. Thus, if one end $A$ of the chain is fixed at the origin of a Cartesian coordinate system $OX$, $OY$, $OZ$ (Fig. 3.5), the other end $B$ will move in a random manner through space. Choosing a small element of volume $d\tau$ in the neighbourhood of any point $P$, the probability that the end $B$ will be found at any instant within this element will be proportional to the volume of the element $d\tau$, and to some function $p(x, y, z)$ representing the density of probability at the point $P$. It is required to determine the form of the function $p(x, y, z)$. For a molecular chain the treatment of this problem in a manner taking proper

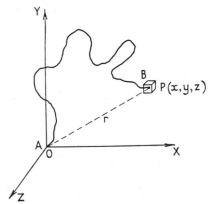

Fig. 3.5. The statistically kinked chain. Specification of probability that the end should fall in the volume element $d\tau$ ($= dxdydz$).

account of the effect of the valence angles presents formidable mathematical difficulties. It is usual, therefore, to ignore the valence angle limitation and to treat the comparatively simple problem of the idealized chain of equal links joined entirely at random, i.e. without regard to valence angle, subsequently introducing the valence angle condition in the form of a suitable correction factor. The conception of completely random joint-ing is to be understood in the sense that the direction in space of any given link in the chain is entirely independent of the direction of neighbouring links, while all directions are equally probable. Thus if the links are regarded as vectors directed outwards from the point $O$, the outer extremities of these vectors will be equally distributed over the surface of a sphere with centre $O$.

The solution to the random chain problem was first given in an approximate form by Kuhn (1934, 1936) and by Guth and Mark (1934). The problem consists essentially in evaluating the

relative number of configurations of the chain, for given values
of $x$, $y$, and $z$. The required probability is proportional to the
number of configurations. For a chain of $n$ links, each of length
$l$, the solution takes the form

$$p(x, y, z)\, dxdydz = (b^3/\pi^{\frac{3}{2}})e^{-b^2(x^2+y^2+z^2)}\, dxdydz, \qquad (3.6)$$

where the parameter $b^2$ has the value $3/2nl^2$. In this formula
$p(x, y, z)$ is the density of probability and $dxdydz$ is the size of
the volume element considered, so that $p(x, y, z)\, dxdydz$ represents the probability that the components of the vector $r$ should
be between $x$ and $x+dx$, $y$ and $y+dy$, $z$ and $z+dz$, respectively.
The derivation of the formula is based on certain approximations which are valid only so long as the distance between the
ends of the chain is not comparable with the maximum possible
extension $nl$; the formula is not applicable when the chain is
nearly fully extended.

The formula (3.6) is of fundamental importance in the theory
of rubber elasticity. Its form is that of the Gaussian error
function, which is of frequent occurrence in statistical problems
connected with the superposition of random effects. It has a
number of interesting properties, some of which will now be
examined.

Firstly, since $x^2+y^2+z^2 = r^2$, the probability density may
be expressed in terms of $r$, the distance of the point $P$ from the
origin $O$, thus

$$p(x, y, z) = (b^3/\pi^{\frac{3}{2}})e^{-b^2(x^2+y^2+z^2)} = (b^3/\pi^{\frac{3}{2}})e^{-b^2r^2}, \qquad (3.7)$$

showing that the distribution is spherically symmetrical, as
would be expected from symmetry considerations. Furthermore, $p(x, y, z)$ is a maximum when $r = 0$, that is when the
two ends of the chain are coincident, and falls continuously as
$r$ increases (cf. Fig. 3.6 (a)). This means that if *one end of the
chain is fixed at the point O, the most probable position of the other
end is at the same point O*. Secondly, the distribution (3.6) can
be represented as the product of three independent probabilities
in $x$, $y$, and $z$ respectively, i.e.

$$p(x, y, z)\, dxdydz = (b^3/\pi^{\frac{3}{2}})e^{-b^2x^2}\, dx \cdot e^{-b^2y^2}\, dy \cdot e^{-b^2z^2}\, dz, \quad (3.6\,a)$$

so that by integrating, for example, over all values of $y$ and $z$, one obtains the distribution function for the component of length in the direction $OX$, which is

$$p(x)\, dx = (b/\sqrt{\pi})e^{-b^2x^2}\, dx. \tag{3.8}$$

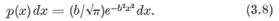

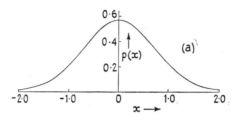

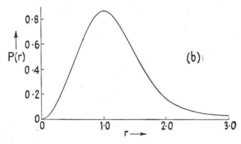

FIG. 3.6. Distribution functions. (a) $p(x) = \text{const. } e^{-b^2x^2}$. (b) $P(r) = \text{const. } r^2e^{-b^2r^2}$.

This function, which is shown in Fig. 3.6 (a), is identical in form with (3.7). The most probable value of $x$ is zero, while the probability of any other value of $x$ is independent of the values of $y$ and $z$.

We come now to a point of particular importance. We have already seen that the probability density, as given by (3.7), is a maximum at the origin, i.e. when the two ends of the chain are coincident. Paradoxically, this does not imply that the most probable length of the chain is zero. For in discussing the probability of any event it is necessary to multiply the probability density by the magnitude of the appropriate volume element $d\tau$. If the whole space is imagined as divided up into elementary cells of equal volume, the cell containing the origin is the one most likely to be occupied by the end $B$ of the chain. In this sense, the most probable position of $B$ is undoubtedly at the origin. But in discussing the probability of a given length of the chain we are concerned with the magnitude, but not with the direction of $r$. If we require to know the probability of a length between $r$ and $r+dr$, we have to allow the end $B$ to fall anywhere within two concentric spheres of radii $r$ and $r+dr$ respectively. The volume enclosed between these spherical surfaces being $4\pi r^2\,dr$, the probability of a length in the interval $dr$ is obtained by multiplying the probability density (3.7) by the size of the volume element under consideration, namely $4\pi r^2\,dr$. The required probability then becomes

$$P(r)\,dr = (b^3/\pi^{\frac{3}{2}})e^{-b^2r^2}\,4\pi r^2\,dr$$
$$= (4b^3/\pi^{\frac{1}{2}})r^2 e^{-b^2r^2}\,dr. \qquad (3.9)$$

This function is depicted in Fig. 3.6 (b). It has a maximum at the point given by

$$r = 1/b = (2n/3)^{\frac{1}{2}}l, \qquad (3.10)$$

which is therefore the most probable value of $r$. Thus, *the most probable length of the randomly kinked chain is proportional to the square root of the number of links.*

The first part of this chapter was concerned with the root-mean-square value of $r$ for various types of chain. For the random chain this quantity may be readily calculated from the distribution function (3.9), since

$$\overline{r^2} = \int_0^\infty r^2 P(r)\,dr,$$

giving 

$$\overline{r^2} = 3/2b^2 = nl^2,$$

or 

$$\sqrt{(\overline{r^2})} = l\sqrt{n}. \qquad (3.11)$$

The root-mean-square length, like the most probable length, is thus proportional to the square root of the number of links in the chain.

As has been stated already, the distribution functions (3.6) and (3.9) are approximations, valid only for $r$-values considerably less than the extended chain length. In practice the approximation is very close up to extensions of about one-third of the fully extended length; for higher extensions one of the more accurate distribution functions discussed in Chapter VI should be used.

*The valence angle correction*

The functions (3.6) and (3.9) contain only one parameter $b$, which determines the 'spread' of the probability curves. It is assumed that any chain of sufficient length will give rise to a distribution function of the general type (3.6), in which the value of $b$ will be determined by its specific geometrical structure. Hence any calculation which permits the determination of $b$ may be assumed also to fix the whole distribution function.

In the first section the root-mean-square length was calculated exactly for particular types of chain. Since it is directly related to $b$ (eqn. 3.11), this quantity therefore enables the scale of the distribution function to be assigned. Thus, for a paraffin-type chain we have from (3.1 a) and (3.11)

$$\frac{1}{b^2} = \frac{2}{3} n l^2 \frac{1+\cos\alpha}{1-\cos\alpha}, \tag{3.12}$$

and the appropriate distribution functions are obtained by inserting the corresponding value of $b$ in equations (3.6) and (3.9) respectively. The same process may be applied to the other chain structures for which values of $\overline{r^2}$ have been given.

In the preceding type of calculation there is no limitation to the closeness of approach of different points of the chain; the volume occupied by the atoms of the chain is not taken into consideration. This means that configurations in which two or more atoms occupy the same volume are included. A method of approach in which such configurations may be excluded, and in which also the effect of a possible interaction energy between neighbouring portions of the chain may be taken into account, has been discussed by Orr (1947). In this method the chain links are laid down on a regular three-dimensional lattice in such a way that no lattice site can be occupied by more than one point of the chain. The number of configurations is obtained by direct counting. Naturally it is only possible to carry out such a direct counting process in the case of quite short chains.

## 4. The entropy of a single chain

In the case where rotation about the bonds of the molecular chain can be considered to be unrestricted by any internal energy barriers, the internal energy of the molecule will be the same for all configurations. With this assumption, the Helmholtz free energy (p. 20) will be determined solely by the entropy term, which in its turn will be proportional to the number of configurations available to the chain in any specified state.

If the chain is considered to be isolated and completely free, all configurations are possible. This condition is approximately realized in the case of a molecule dissolved in a large excess of a neutral liquid, i.e. a liquid such that there is no heat of mixing of the polymer and solvent molecules. If, on the other hand, there are certain restrictions imposed on the free motion of the chain, the number of available configurations will be reduced. The simplest, and from the point of view of the theory of elasticity the most appropriate, restriction which can be envisaged consists in fixing the two ends of the molecule at specified points, or more precisely, fixing one end at the point $O$, while the other end is confined to a small volume element $d\tau$ in the neighbourhood of a point $P$ at a distance $r$ from $O$. Subject to this restriction, the number of configurations available to the chain is proportional to the density of probability at the point $P$ (given by eqn. 3.7) multiplied by the size of the volume element $d\tau$. The truth of this statement follows at once from the manner of deriving the probability density. If we now let the point $P$ take different positions, while $d\tau$ is maintained constant, the relative number of configurations will, from (3.7), depend only on $r$, and will be given by $e^{-b^2 r^2}$. The entropy, being proportional to the logarithm of the number of available configurations, will therefore be (Kuhn, 1936)

$$s = c - kb^2 r^2, \tag{3.13}$$

where $c$ is an arbitrary constant and $k$ is Boltzmann's constant. The presence of the constant $c$ (which includes the size of the volume element $d\tau$) indicates that we are concerned only with relative probabilities or with differences of entropy, and not with absolute values of these quantities.

The result (3.13) shows the entropy to have its maximum

value when the two ends of the chain are coincident ($r = 0$), and to become continuously smaller with increasing separation of the ends.

It is important to bear in mind that there is no unique sense in which the entropy of a molecule is to be defined, but that any expression for the entropy (as for the corresponding probability) must be regarded as applicable only in so far as the specified conditions of the problem under examination correspond with the restrictive conditions assumed in or implied by the entropy calculation. A chain does not possess an entropy by the mere fact of having a specified configuration, but only by virtue of the large number of configurations accessible to it under specified conditions of restraint. If these conditions consist only in the location of the end-points of the chain at specified positions, then the appropriate expression for the entropy is (3.13).

## 5. The tension on a chain

For a chain whose ends are located at specified points separated by a distance $r$, the entropy $s$ is given by (3.13), and the corresponding Helmholtz free energy by $-Ts$. The work required to move one end from a distance $r$ to a distance $r+dr$ with respect to the other is, by definition, equal to the change in Helmholtz free energy, and therefore

$$\frac{dW}{dr} = \frac{dA}{dr} = -T\frac{ds}{dr}. \tag{3.14}$$

Inserting the value of $ds/dr$ obtained by differentiation of the entropy function (3.13) we obtain

$$dW/dr = 2kTb^2r. \tag{3.15}$$

Since work has to be performed to change the length from $r$ to $r+dr$, it follows that there must be a tensile force $f$ acting along the direction of $r$. The work done by this force in a virtual displacement $dr$ is $f dr$; the magnitude of the tension is therefore (from 3.15)

$$f = 2kTb^2r. \tag{3.16}$$

Thus, *a molecule with its ends fixed at specified points is acted*

*on by a tensile force in the direction of the line joining its ends
and proportional to the length of that line* (Fig. 3.7).

Since the tension in a chain is proportional to its length, the
molecule may be regarded as possessing an elasticity governed
by Hooke's law (stress proportional to strain). It corresponds,
in fact, to a classical spring of zero unstretched length.

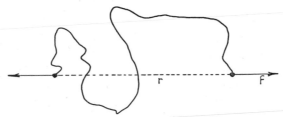

FIG. 3.7. The tension in a chain whose ends are fixed in position is
proportional to the distance $r$.

The spring analogy must not, however, be taken too literally.
Owing to its statistical origin, the tension in a chain whose end-
points are located at fixed positions will be subject to continual
fluctuations, like the pressure exerted by a gas on the walls of
its containing vessel. Likewise, if the molecule is subjected to
a constant tension, its length will be a fluctuating quantity.
These fluctuations will become relatively less important as the
number of links in the chain is increased. The formula (3.16)
represents the *average* value of the tension over a period of
time.

A further point to be remembered is that the linear force-
extension relation (3.16) is subject to the same limitations as
the Gaussian distribution function from which it is derived.
It is therefore valid only so long as the distance between the
ends of the chain is not so large as to be comparable with its
fully extended length. This means in practice (as will be shown
in Chapter VI) that the distance $r$ should not be more than
about one-third of the fully-extended length. For higher extensions the Gaussian approximation becomes increasingly inaccurate and must be replaced by a more accurate distribution
function.

# CHAPTER IV

# THE ELASTICITY OF A MOLECULAR NETWORK

## 1. Fundamental assumptions

IF a piece of well-vulcanized rubber is subjected to a simple elongation, the relation between the tensile force and the extension has the characteristic form shown in Fig. 1.1 (p. 2). The abscissae in this diagram represent the extension as a percentage of the original length, while the ordinates refer to the force *per unit area of the unstrained cross-section*. This is the method of plotting normally used in the industry. The features of this curve are (1) an initial bending over towards the extension axis, and (2) a final upward curvature in the region immediately preceding the breaking strain. Much ingenuity has been expended in the attempt to explain these characteristic features, in which rubber differs so strikingly from a normal elastic solid obeying Hooke's law, but it is only in recent years that, with the help of the statistical theory, their significance has become fully understood.

It is perhaps unfortunate that interest in the form of the stress-strain relations for rubber has been concentrated primarily on simple elongation, because the stress-strain relations for other types of deformation, such as, for example, compression or shear, have quite different forms which are equally significant from the theoretical standpoint. One of the most interesting aspects of the statistical theory is that it has provided a basis for the correlation of the behaviour of rubber under different types of strain. It has, in fact, led to the derivation of general formulae for the principal stresses in terms of the most general homogeneous strain, and has in this way made an important contribution to the formulation of a general theory of large elastic deformations.

As explained in Chapter I, the theory is based on the conception of vulcanized rubber as an assembly of long-chain molecules, linked together at a relatively small number of points (points of vulcanization or cross-linkage) so as to form an irregular three-dimensional network. The statistical method of approach has already been applied to the single chain or structural element of the network; the problem now is concerned with the application of the same kind of approach to the more complicated problem of the whole assembly of chains comprising the network. As with the single chain, the discussion will be limited in the first place to the approximate theory, corresponding to what has been called the Gaussian region of extension.

Since the appearance of Kuhn's original theory (Kuhn, 1936) a number of methods have been proposed for the solution of the network problem, most of which have led to essentially the same results. Particular mention should be made of the contributions to the subject by James and Guth (1943), Wall (1942), Flory and Rehner (1943), and the author (Treloar, 1943*a*, 1943*b*), as a result of which the theory may now be regarded as well established, at least in its essential outlines. There has been much discussion between authors concerning the merits of the arguments upon which particular forms of the theory have been based, and on many of the finer aspects of the problem there is still room for legitimate differences of opinion. Some of these differences will be referred to in the course of this chapter, but their full consideration would probably be confusing rather than helpful to the reader who is not a specialist in this particular field, and will not be attempted. Instead, one particular form of the theory will be chosen for rather detailed consideration, while certain aspects of some of the other forms will be discussed in connexion with points of special interest which may arise.

The selected theory is essentially that of Kuhn (1936), somewhat modified and extended by the author (Treloar, 1943*a*, 1943*b*). It is based on the following assumptions:

1. The chains forming the network all have the same contour† length.

2. The distribution of chain displacement lengths in the unstrained state is represented by the Gaussian function.

† Flory's nomenclature is adopted here to distinguish between the length measured along the chain (*chain contour length*) and the rectilinear distance between its ends (*chain displacement length*).

3. The volume remains unchanged on deformation.

4. The effect of the deformation is to change the components of displacement length of each chain in the same ratio as the corresponding dimensions of the bulk rubber.

Before proceeding, the significance of these assumptions must be examined. Assumption 1 is introduced for simplicity, but is not essential. By 'chain' is meant that portion of a molecule included between successive junction points along its length. Assumption 2 is based upon the following argument. In the rubber prior to vulcanization each molecule will exist in a purely random form, in which the distance between its ends, or between any two points along its length, will be described by the Gaussian probability formula (eqn. 3.9). If vulcanization takes place by random cross-linking of points of neighbouring chains, it would appear reasonable to assume that it will not affect the instantaneous form of the molecules concerned, and hence that the distribution of chain displacement lengths will be the same as for a system of free chains of the same contour lengths. This argument, though frequently employed, is not strictly valid, as we shall see later (p. 66). Assumption 3 is based on observation and is certainly very nearly true. The fourth assumption is entirely arbitrary, though if some assumption about the transformation of chain displacement lengths on deformation has to be introduced, this particular one is obviously the simplest and most natural. If the components of length of each chain change in the same ratio as the corresponding dimensions of the bulk rubber, the junction points will be displaced exactly like particles embedded in an elastic continuum. This type of displacement is referred to by Kuhn as an 'affine' (i.e. 'corresponding') deformation of chain components.

The calculation of the stress-strain relationships of the rubber proceeds by the following stages. First, from the distribution of chain displacement lengths in the unstrained state, the entropy in the unstrained state is calculated by summation of the entropies of the individual chains. Secondly, using assumptions 3 and 4, the corresponding entropy in the strained state is derived. In the third step the work of deformation is derived from the difference of entropy in these two states. The final step consists in the calculation of the stress-strain relations; these are obtained by differentiation with respect to the strains of the function representing the work of deformation.

## 2. Detailed development of the theory

*The work of deformation*

Kuhn dealt originally with the case of a simple elongation of the rubber, but it is no more difficult to treat the case of the

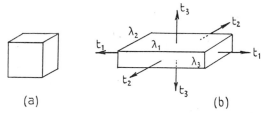

(a)                                    (b)

Fig. 4.1. Pure homogeneous strain. (*a*) The unstrained state.
(*b*) The strained state.

most general homogeneous strain. By this is meant a strain characterized by three principal extension ratios in three principal directions which are mutually perpendicular to one another. Under such a strain a unit cube (Fig. 4.1) is transformed into a rectangular parallelepiped with three unequal edges. Denoting these edges by $\lambda_1$, $\lambda_2$, and $\lambda_3$ we may call $\lambda_1$, $\lambda_2$, and $\lambda_3$ the *principal extension ratios*, whose magnitude defines the strain. (These extension ratios may be greater than 1, corresponding to a stretch, or less than 1, corresponding to a compression.) Alternatively, a sphere of unit radius becomes transformed by a homogeneous strain into an ellipsoid, the *strain ellipsoid*, having three unequal axes of lengths $2\lambda_1$, $2\lambda_2$, and $2\lambda_3$. The axes of the strain ellipsoid define the directions of the principal strains.

For an affine deformation of chain displacement lengths a chain whose end-to-end distance was originally represented by the vector $\mathbf{r}$ (Fig. 4.2), having components $x$, $y$, and $z$, is transformed to a vector length $\mathbf{r}'$ with components $x'$, $y'$, and $z'$, where

$$x' = \lambda_1 x; \qquad y' = \lambda_2 y; \qquad z' = \lambda_3 z, \qquad (4.1)$$

the axes of coordinates being chosen to coincide with the directions of the principal strains. From assumptions 1 and 2 the

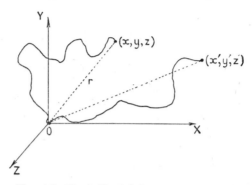

Fig. 4.2. The 'affine' deformation of chains.

number of chains in the unstrained state having length components in the range $dx$, $dy$, $dz$ is

$$dN = N(b^3/\pi^{\frac{3}{2}})e^{-b^2(x^2+y^2+z^2)}\,dx\,dy\,dz, \qquad (4.2)$$

and by equation (3.13) (p. 53) each of these has an entropy

$$s_0 = c - kb^2(x^2+y^2+z^2). \qquad (4.3)$$

The total entropy $S_0$ in the unstrained state is therefore

$$S_0 = \int s_0 \, dN$$

$$= \frac{Nb^3}{\pi^{\frac{3}{2}}} \int\!\!\!\int\!\!\!\int_{-\infty}^{+\infty} [c - kb^2(x^2+y^2+z^2)]e^{-b^2(x^2+y^2+z^2)}\,dx\,dy\,dz. \qquad (4.4)$$

This integral (in spite of its cumbersome appearance) reduces to a very simple form.† The result is

$$S_0 = N(c - 3k/2). \qquad (4.5)$$

Each chain in the group $dN$ referred to in equation (4.2) will as a result of the deformation suffer a change in its components

† See appendix to this chapter.

of length in accordance with the transformation (4.1). Its entropy in the strained state will therefore be

$$s = c - kb^2(\lambda_1^2 x^2 + \lambda_2^2 y^2 + \lambda_3^2 z^2), \tag{4.6}$$

so that the total entropy in the strained state becomes

$$S = \int s\, dN$$

$$= \frac{Nb^3}{\pi^{\frac{3}{2}}} \int\!\!\int\!\!\int_{-\infty}^{+\infty} [c - kb^2(\lambda_1^2 x^2 + \lambda_2^2 y^2 + \lambda_3^2 z^2)] e^{-b^2(x^2 + y^2 + z^2)}\, dx\, dy\, dz \tag{4.7}$$

or $$S = N[c - \tfrac{1}{2}k(\lambda_1^2 + \lambda_2^2 + \lambda_3^2)]. \tag{4.7a}$$

The required entropy difference between the strained and unstrained states is therefore, from (4.4) and (4.7),

$$S - S_0 = -\tfrac{1}{2}Nk(\lambda_1^2 + \lambda_2^2 + \lambda_3^2 - 3). \tag{4.8}$$

Assuming no internal energy change to accompany the strain, the work of deformation or *stored energy*† per unit volume becomes

$$W = \tfrac{1}{2}NkT(\lambda_1^2 + \lambda_2^2 + \lambda_3^2 - 3) \tag{4.9}$$

$$= \tfrac{1}{2}G(\lambda_1^2 + \lambda_2^2 + \lambda_3^2 - 3). \tag{4.9a}$$

Equation (4.9a) may be thought of as the fundamental relation by which the elastic properties of a rubber in the Gaussian region are completely defined. The stored energy is of course proportional to the absolute temperature, but contains only a single physical constant $G$ related to the material. This constant is itself proportional to $N$, the number of chains per unit volume.

This is a very important conclusion. It shows that the physical properties of a rubber, in so far as they can be represented by the statistical theory, are independent of the chemical nature of the molecules of which it is composed, being determined only by the number of chains, or alternatively the number of junction points in the network. The quantity $N$ is also related to the 'molecular weight' $M_c$ of the chains in such a way that we may write

$$NkT = \rho RT/M_c, \tag{4.10}$$

---

† The word 'energy' is here used in the mechanical sense. Thermodynamically the work of deformation is stored 'free energy'.

where $R$ is the gas constant. In this connexion $M_c$ is to be understood as the weight of the portion of a molecule lying between successive junction points.

### The principal stresses

In the state of pure homogeneous strain depicted in Fig. 4.1 there are three principal stresses acting in directions parallel to the principal axes of strain on planes represented by the faces of the rectangular block. Denoting these principal stresses by $t_1$, $t_2$, and $t_3$ in the directions corresponding to $\lambda_1$, $\lambda_2$, and $\lambda_3$ respectively, it can be shown (Treloar, 1943$b$) that equation (4.9$a$) leads to the following general stress-strain relations:

$$t_1 - t_2 = G(\lambda_1^2 - \lambda_2^2)$$
$$t_2 - t_3 = G(\lambda_2^2 - \lambda_3^2). \qquad (4.11)$$

If the principal strains are given, these relations permit the derivation of the difference between any two of the principal stresses, but not the absolute values of these quantities. Alternatively, we may write

$$t_1 = G\lambda_1^2 + p; \qquad t_2 = G\lambda_2^2 + p; \qquad t_3 = G\lambda_3^2 + p, \qquad (4.11\,a)$$

where $p$ is an arbitrary stress in the nature of a hydrostatic pressure (since it is the same on all faces). Equations (4.11) or the alternative forms (4.11$a$) therefore imply that *the principal stresses are indeterminate to the extent of a superimposed hydrostatic pressure of arbitrary value.* This result is in no way surprising, since it is a direct consequence of our initial assumption (3) of constancy of volume during the deformation, an assumption which is equivalent to the statement that the rubber is incompressible. That being so, the addition of an arbitrary hydrostatic pressure will have no effect on the strains, and the stresses are necessarily to this extent indeterminate.

In many problems this degree of indeterminacy is removed by the prior knowledge of one or more of the principal stresses. When this is the case the general stress-strain equations (4.11) admit of a unique solution. Examples of this kind of problem appear in the following pages.

## 3. Refinement of the theory

### The model of James and Guth

The foregoing treatment, leading to the derivation of the general stored-energy relation (4.9), has the merit of directness and simplicity and is based on a physical model which appears to be at least in approximate conformity with reality. But in certain of its details it is rather too crude, and various refinements and modifications have been suggested from time to time. Some aspects of these proposals and alternatives will now be discussed.

The first and most fundamental objection to the Kuhn theory is that the junction points of the network are conceived of as fixed at particular points in space. The freedom of movement of the system is thus limited to the lengths of chain between these fixed points, and the function used to represent the entropy of the individual chains corresponds precisely with this conception, because, as shown in the preceding chapter, this function defines the entropy of a chain whose extremities occupy fixed positions. This conception of the network is, however, inadequate because the junction points are not actually fixed. A method of approach corresponding much more closely with physical reality has been worked out in very great detail by James and Guth (1943). These authors visualize the network as a system of chains joined together at certain points exactly as in Kuhn's model, but the junction points are themselves considered to take part in the micro-Brownian motion of the chain elements. More precisely, the only junction points whose positions are initially specified are those which are located on the boundary surfaces of the rubber. Complete statistical freedom is allowed to all other junction points, subject of course to the necessary internal restrictions imposed by the mutual interconnexions of the chains. The system of junction points thus comprises a certain number of fixed junction points, whose positions in space define the state of strain, and a very much larger number of fluctuating junction points. The problem involved in the derivation of the stress-strain properties, or stored-energy function of the network, is essentially the computation of the total number of configurations of all the chains, subject to the condition that the fixed junction points lie on specified planes, while all other junction points may occupy all possible positions.

It is clear that James and Guth's model corresponds more nearly with the actual physical structure of the rubber. For any given junction point is nothing else than the point at which four chains meet, and if the chains themselves are subject to random fluctuations, the same consideration must apply to the junction points. There is, in fact, no physical means whereby the junction points could be maintained in fixed relative positions in the manner required by Kuhn's theory.

It is not surprising that the problem of calculating the number of configurations available to the whole network, subject to certain boundary conditions, should involve a rather lengthy mathematical argument. This argument will not be reproduced in detail, but a summary will be given of the principal conclusions arrived at by James and Guth in the course of their analysis of the problem, since these conclusions reveal a number of particularly significant physical properties of the network.

1. The fluctuations of position of any junction point in a network of Gaussian chains may be described by a Gaussian probability function. The mean value of the fluctuations of any junction point is independent of the amount of strain.

2. The average force between any two adjacent junction points is the same as if both were fixed at their most probable positions.

3. The average forces exerted by the network are the same as would be produced if each chain were replaced by a classical elastic spring exerting a tension proportional to its length.

4. As a corollary to (3), if the network is subjected to a homogeneous strain, the average positions of the junction points will be displaced as if they were embedded in an elastic continuum.

5. The forces exerted by the network are the same whether any given junction point is treated as free, or as fixed at its most probable position.

6. For the calculation of the forces acting on the bounding surfaces, the network may be replaced by a fictitious system of three independent sets of Gaussian chains parallel to the three coordinate axes.

These and other results are proved by a rigorous analysis which is quite general in that it involves no assumption regarding the distribution of chain lengths or the detailed structure of the network. Proposition 4 establishes a basis for Kuhn's assumption of an affine deformation of chains, while 5 proves that the neglect of the fluctuations of the junction points has no effect on the resultant stress-strain relations. The latter result follows from the fact that the fluctuations of a given point are unaffected by the strain; the term in the entropy corresponding to the fluctuations of the junction points is therefore the same in both the strained and unstrained states, and so does not affect the difference of entropy in the two states.

In the previous chapter it was shown that a single chain could be compared in its elastic properties with a classical elastic spring. Proposition 3 above carries the analogy still further. From this result it follows also that the ideal network would, in the absence of other forces, collapse to zero volume, since each pair of junction points is under the action of a tension tending to draw them together. In the actual rubber this tendency is balanced by the mutual repulsive forces between the atoms. Thus James and Guth distinguish, in the actual rubber, two quite different sets of forces, the first being those related to the configurational entropy of the network, and the second being the internal pressure developed in the rubber by interatomic forces of the same kind as those existing in an ordinary liquid. The assumption involved in the statistical treatment is that the free energy changes are associated only with the network configurations, and not at all with the interatomic forces. This is likely to be true to a first approximation; so long, in fact, as the changes in volume of the system are of negligible amount, so that the rubber may be considered incompressible. When this condition is satisfied, an arbitrary hydrostatic pressure may be introduced as required to balance the tension due to the network on any surface on which there is no external stress.

From the close correspondence between the basic assumptions of Kuhn's theory and the conclusions arrived at by the more elaborate treatment of James and Guth, it is to be expected that both theories will lead to essentially the same final results. This is indeed found to be so, for James and Guth's expression for the stored energy is identical with (4.9) except for the factor $NkT$, for which is substituted the more general expression

$$G = kT \sum_\tau n_\tau \lambda_\tau, \tag{4.12}$$

where $n_\tau$ is the number of statistical links in the $\tau$th chain, and $\lambda_\tau$ is the ratio of its mean displacement length in the unstrained state to its fully extended length. For the case where the displacement lengths are distributed in the same way as if the chains were free (i.e. isolated) the expression (4.12) reduces to

$$G = NkT$$

whether or not the chains are all of the same contour length. It has been pointed out, however (Guth, James, and Mark, 1946), that a consideration of the process of network formation leads to a distribution differing from that corresponding to free chains, and they prefer to leave the constant in the less specific form

$$G = \gamma NkT = \gamma \rho RT/M_c, \tag{4.12 a}$$

where $\gamma$ is a numerical factor whose precise value will depend on the detailed structure of the network, and $M_c$ is the mean molecular weight of the chains. This point is of some importance in view of attempts which have been made to correlate the experimental values of the modulus $G$ with the number of cross-linkages in the rubber, discussed in Chapter V.

That the actual distribution of displacement lengths in the unstrained state should differ from the distribution for free chains may be demonstrated by the example of a molecule which is cross-linked at a number of points in its length to an already partially formed network. The first cross-link will restrain one point of the molecule, but will not alter the number

of configurations available to it. The second linkage will introduce a further restraint which will interfere with the configurations available to the intermediate length of chain, since the
fluctuations of position of the second junction point with respect
to the first will be restricted. This being so, the spatial distribution function for any intermediate point referred, say, to the
first junction point will no longer correspond with the distribution function for a free chain. In this respect, therefore, Kuhn's
assumption concerning the distribution of chain displacement
lengths is not strictly true.†

Kuhn himself has questioned the numerical significance of the
factor $NkT$ in equation (4.9), but for a different reason. In his
original work he considered that the entropy of a single chain
in the network should depend not only on its vector length $r_1$,
as represented by equation (4.3), but also on its 'breadth' and
'thickness', as represented by the distribution of points respectively half-way along the chain and one-quarter of the way
along, measured from either end. The inclusion of these two
additional terms in the entropy function leads to a modified value
of the modulus $G$ in (4.9 a), i.e.

$$G = \tfrac{7}{3}NkT. \tag{4.12 b}$$

As a result of criticisms brought against the inclusion of these
additional terms, particularly by the author (1943 a), on the
ground that the only points of restraint on the motion of the
chain are the junction points, or end-points, Kuhn (1946) no
longer claims quantitative significance for the factor $\tfrac{7}{3}$ in (4.12 b).
He points out, however, that the chains are not in fact entirely
free at all points other than their end-points, on account of the
presence of 'foreign' junction points in the neighbourhood of
a given chain. Interferences due to this cause may be regarded
effectively as additional or 'steric' junction points, which,
though less definite than the primary chemical junction points,
must affect the modulus $G$ in the direction of making it more
nearly equal to $\tfrac{7}{3}NkT$ than to $NkT$.

† Since this was written a detailed discussion of this question has appeared
(James and Guth, 1947).

*Flory's treatment of network defects*

A rather more comprehensive study of certain types of departure of the real network from the idealized model has been carried out by Flory (1944). Attention is drawn, in particular, to three types of defect. The first, represented in Fig. 4.3 (*a*), arises from the possibility of interlooping or entanglements of the chains. Entanglements of this kind, by restricting the

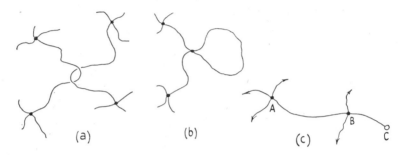

FIG. 4.3. Types of network defect. (Flory, 1944.)

number of configurations available to the network, have an effect comparable with that of chemical cross-linkages. Another type of defect occurs as a result of the linkage of two points in a single chain (Fig. 4.3 (*b*)), with the formation of a closed loop. Such a loop contributes nothing to the elastic reaction of the network; ineffective linkages of this type should therefore be omitted in the calculation of the modulus. A third type of defect arises from the presence of chains which are attached to the network at one end only. The idealized model assumes that all chains are attached at each end; this will be strictly true only if the original molecules in the unvulcanized rubber are of infinite length. For molecules of finite length there will be, in general, two terminal chains for each primary molecule. This is illustrated by Fig. 4.3 (*c*), in which *BC* represents the terminal segment of a molecule having cross-linkages at *A* and *B*. Such terminal chains are not elements of the network structure.

Of these network defects, the only one which can be treated in a fairly simple manner is the last. Starting from $N$ primary uncross-linked molecules, Flory argues that $N-1$ intermolecular linkages will be sufficient to produce what is effectively a single ramified structure in which there are no closed loops. Additional cross-links must result in the formation of closed loops or network circuits. There will be one loop, or two network chains, for each such additional cross-linkage. Denoting the total number of cross-linkages by $\frac{1}{2}\nu_0$ and the number of effective or network-forming linkages by $\frac{1}{2}\nu$ and writing $N$ for $N-1$, it follows that

$$\frac{1}{2}\nu = \frac{1}{2}\nu_0 - N.$$

The effective number of chains will be twice this quantity, i.e.

$$\nu = \nu_0(1-2N/\nu_0) = \nu_0(1-2M_c/M), \tag{4.13}$$

where $M$ is the molecular weight of the primary molecules and $M_c$ is the average chain molecular weight, inclusive of terminal chains. This result is obviously applicable only if the number of cross-links is sufficiently large for all the molecules to be mutually connected into a single structure.

The effect of other network defects is represented by Flory by the introduction of a further factor $g$. Thus the final expression for the modulus $G$ is

$$G = g\frac{\rho RT}{M_c}(1-2M_c/M). \tag{4.14}$$

This equation is used for the interpretation of Flory's experimental data, which will be considered in the following chapter.

## 4. Particular stress-strain relations

In this section the application of the general stress-strain relations (4.11) to certain simple types of homogeneous strain will be considered.

### (a) Simple elongation

Simple elongation is the type of strain in most common use in routine tests on rubber. In this type of strain one dimension of the initial unit cube (Fig. 4.4 (a)) is increased in the ratio $\alpha$, while the other two dimensions are reduced in the ratio $1/\sqrt{\alpha}$, so as to maintain the volume unchanged. The principal extension ratios are therefore

$$\lambda_1 = \alpha; \qquad \lambda_2 = \lambda_3 = 1/\sqrt{\alpha}. \tag{4.15}$$

If $f$ is the tensile force per unit cross-sectional area, *measured in the undeformed state*, the stress referred to the actual area in the deformed state will be $\alpha f$. This corresponds to the stress $t_1$ in equations (4.11). Since the other two principal stresses,

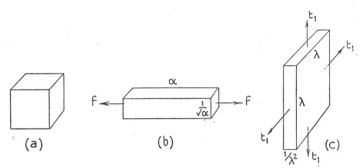

FIG. 4.4. Types of strain. (*a*) Unstrained state. (*b*) Simple elongation.
(*c*) Uniform two-dimensional extension.

$t_2$ and $t_3$, are zero, introduction of (4.15) into (4.11) gives the required relation between force and elongation ratio $\alpha$. Thus

$$t_1 - t_3 = \alpha f = G(\alpha^2 - 1/\alpha), \qquad (4.16)$$

or
$$f = G(\alpha - 1/\alpha^2). \qquad (4.16\,a)$$

(*b*) *Unidirectional compression*

The case of a compression in one direction with free expansion in the other two directions is formally identical with simple elongation, except that in this case $\alpha$ is less than 1. The compressive force per unit area, *measured in the undeformed state*, is correspondingly given by (4.16 $a$).

Thus both elongation and compression are represented by a single curve, having the form shown in Fig. 4.5. This form accounts qualitatively for the initial curvature of the experimental force-elongation relation (Fig. 1.1), though it completely fails to represent the final upward bend of the experimental curve. As we shall see later, however, the explanation of this final upward bend is provided by a more exact statistical treatment, applicable to the region of high extension of the chains, or non-Gaussian region, which is specifically excluded in the elementary theory. The formulae derived from the elementary theory are therefore inapplicable in the region of very large strains.

Since the stress-strain relation for a rubber in elongation or compression is non-linear, the classical conception of a Young's modulus is not applicable, except in the limiting case of in-

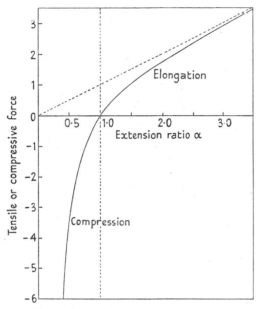

Fig. 4.5. Theoretical relation between force and extension (or compression) ratio, $f = G(\alpha - 1/\alpha^2)$, with $G = 1\cdot0$.

finitesimally small strains. In this limiting case Young's modulus $E$ has the value

$$E = (df/d\alpha)_{\alpha=1} = 3G.$$

### Uniform two-dimensional extension

In this type of strain the rubber is stretched by equal amounts in two directions at right angles (Fig. 4.4 (c)). Such a strain occurs, for example, in the inflation of a spherical balloon. The strain is actually the same as in a unidirectional compression; the only difference is in the method of applying the stress. If the stretch ratio is $\lambda$, we have

$$\lambda_1 = \lambda_2 = \lambda; \qquad \lambda_3 = 1/\lambda^2,$$

and the stress in the direction of $\lambda_1$ or $\lambda_2$ is, from equations (4.11),

$$t_1 = G(\lambda^2 - 1/\lambda^4). \qquad (4.17)$$

In the case of a sheet of original thickness $d_0$, the total force $f$ acting across a section of unit length cut at right angles to the plane of the sheet is equal to the product of the stress $t_1$ and the area $d_0/\lambda^2$, so that

$$f = Gd_0(1 - 1/\lambda^6). \qquad (4.17\,a)$$

In the uniform two-dimensional extension the lengths of all lines in the plane of the extension are changed in the same ratio, and the stress is the same on all sections normal to the sheet. If the sheet is thin, this stress is analogous to a surface tension. For extensions exceeding $\lambda = 2$ the tension, as represented by (4.17 $a$), becomes substantially independent of the extension.

### Shear

A shear is a two-dimensional type of strain; that is to say, a strain in which one dimension of the body remains unchanged, and in which also the volume remains unchanged.

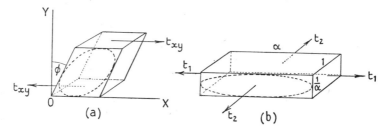

FIG. 4.6. ($a$) Simple shear. ($b$) Pure shear.

Simple shear may be represented by the sliding of planes parallel to a given plane by an amount proportional to their distance from a given plane. Thus, the lateral faces of a cube are transformed by simple shear into parallelograms (Fig. 4.6 ($a$)), and the amount of shear is measured by the tangent of the angle $\phi$ through which a vertical edge is tilted. The stress $t_{xy}$ acting tangentially on the faces parallel to the plane of the slide is known as a tangential or shearing stress.

Simple shear is not easy to represent in terms of the principal extension ratios, because the directions of the principal axes of the strain ellipsoid are not simply related to the plane of sliding. For this reason it is easier to work with the type of strain known as *pure shear* (Fig. 4.6 (*b*)). In general, a pure strain is one which involves extensions in three directions, without rotation; the most general homogeneous strain involves both extensions and rotations. A pure shear is defined as a pure homogeneous strain in which one of the principal extensions is zero and the volume is unchanged. Hence if the extension ratio $\lambda_1$ is equal to $\alpha$, while $\lambda_2 = 1$, the third extension ratio $\lambda_3$ is necessarily $1/\alpha$.

It may be shown† that a simple shear is equivalent to a pure shear plus a rotation. If $\sigma$ is the amount of the shear, we have, for simple shear,

$$\sigma = \tan\phi, \tag{4.18 a}$$

while for pure shear

$$\sigma = \alpha - 1/\alpha. \tag{4.18 b}$$

Taking the case of a pure shear in which the stress in the direction $\lambda_3$ is zero, the principal stresses $t_1$ and $t_2$ in the other two directions are both tensile (Fig. 4.6 (*b*)); their magnitude is given directly from equations (4.11), i.e.

$$\left.\begin{array}{l} t_1 = G(\alpha^2 - 1/\alpha^2), \\ t_2 = G(1 - 1/\alpha^2). \end{array}\right\} \tag{4.19}$$

These are the actual stresses, or forces per unit area in the strained state. If $f_1$ and $f_2$ are the corresponding forces on faces of unit area before deformation, we have (since $f_1 = t_1 \lambda_2 \lambda_3 = t_1/\lambda_1$),

$$\left.\begin{array}{l} f_1 = G(\alpha - 1/\alpha^3), \\ f_2 = G(1 - 1/\alpha^2). \end{array}\right\} \tag{4.19 a}$$

The case of *simple shear* is more easily handled by means of the stored-energy function (4.9 *a*), which gives for the work of deformation per unit volume

$$W = \tfrac{1}{2}G(\alpha^2 + 1/\alpha^2 - 2), \tag{4.20}$$

† Love, *Mathematical Theory of Elasticity* (Camb. Univ. Press), chap. 1.

which, in terms of the amount of shear $\sigma$ (eqn. 4.18$b$), becomes

$$W = \tfrac{1}{2}G\sigma^2. \tag{4.21}$$

Assuming that the work done on the body is due entirely to the shearing stress $t_{xy}$,† it follows that

$$t_{xy} = dW/d\sigma = G\sigma, \tag{4.22}$$

which means that the shearing stress is proportional to the shear strain. Hooke's law is therefore obeyed in simple shear, and the quantity $G$ corresponds to the modulus of rigidity in the classical theory of elasticity. The statistical theory thus leads to the interesting result that rubber should obey Hooke's law in shear, though not in elongation or compression.

## 5. The stored-energy function for a swollen rubber

Equation (4.8), giving the entropy of deformation of the network, does not actually require for its derivation the assumption of incompressibility of the rubber. Indirectly, however, this assumption is involved, since it is only when the volume remains constant that we are entitled to take account only of the configurational entropy, and to ignore the effect of the forces between atoms and molecules. The incompressibility condition is, however, directly involved in the derivation of the stress-strain relations from the stored-energy function.

If there are volume changes, it is still legitimate to regard equation (4.8) as a valid expression of the *configurational entropy*. Hence, if the rubber is isotropically expanded by a swelling agent, the change in the network entropy due to the swelling will be

$$\Delta S_1 = -\tfrac{1}{2}Nk(3\lambda_0^2 - 3), \tag{4.23}$$

where $\lambda_0$ is the linear swelling ratio. If the rubber is unstressed, this negative entropy change on swelling is compensated by the positive, and generally much larger entropy (or free energy) change due to the mixing of the rubber and liquid molecules. The effect of straining the swollen rubber is to change its dimensions to $\lambda_1'$, $\lambda_2'$, and $\lambda_3'$; its configurational entropy referred to the unstrained unswollen state is therefore

$$\Delta S_0' = -\tfrac{1}{2}Nk(\lambda_1'^2 + \lambda_2'^2 + \lambda_3'^2 - 3). \tag{4.24}$$

---

† There are in fact other stresses present, but they do no work (see Chap. XIII).

By difference, the entropy of deformation of the swollen rubber is

$$\Delta S' = \Delta S_0' - \Delta S_1 = -\tfrac{1}{2}Nk(\lambda_1'^2 + \lambda_2'^2 + \lambda_3'^2 - 3\lambda_0^2), \quad (4.25)$$

which, when the strains are referred to the swollen state by writing $\lambda_1 = \lambda_1'/\lambda_0$, etc., becomes

$$\Delta S' = -\tfrac{1}{2}Nk\lambda_0^2(\lambda_1^2 + \lambda_2^2 + \lambda_3^2 - 3). \quad (4.26)$$

This equation represents the configurational entropy of deformation for the swollen network. If the degree of swelling is the same in the strained and unstrained states, we may assume that the free energy of mixing is the same in both states, and consider the expression (4.26) to be the total entropy change on deformation. The work of deformation of the swollen rubber then becomes simply $-T\,\Delta S'$, where $\Delta S'$ is given by (4.26) and $N$ is the number of chains per unit volume of the *unswollen* rubber. The work of deformation per unit volume of the *swollen* rubber is, consequently,

$$W = -T\Delta S'\,\lambda_0^{-3} = \tfrac{1}{2}NkT\lambda_0^{-1}(\lambda_1^2 + \lambda_2^2 + \lambda_3^2 - 3)$$
$$= \tfrac{1}{2}NkTv_r^{\frac{1}{3}}(\lambda_1^2 + \lambda_2^2 + \lambda_3^2 - 3), \quad (4.27)$$

where $v_r$ is the volume fraction of rubber in the mixture of rubber and liquid.

From equation (4.27) it follows that the form of the stress-strain relations is unaffected by swelling, but the modulus $G$, and therefore all the stresses are reduced in the ratio $v_r^{\frac{1}{3}}$, i.e. inversely as the cube root of the swelling ratio.

## 6. Conclusion

For the sake of simplicity, and in order to preserve continuity in the argument, the matter presented in this chapter is not arranged in an order corresponding to the historical development of the subject, and for the same reasons the emphasis attached to particular theories or aspects of the subject does not necessarily correspond with the significance or importance of those particular theories for the development of the subject at the time of their appearance. This brief historical note is added in order to correct some of the defects inherent in the form of presentation adopted.

Though Kuhn was the first to attack the problem of the elasticity of a molecular network (Kuhn, 1936), the form of the stress-strain relation for simple elongation which he derived was applicable only to infinitesimally small strains. The discovery of the curved relation (4.16 a) governing large deformations in extension or compression was due to Guth and James, and was originally published with an abbreviated method of derivation (Guth and James, 1941). The same relation was derived by a different method by Wall, who was also the first to treat the problem of shear on the basis of the statistical theory (Wall, 1942). Soon after this the author drew attention to the close similarity in the underlying concepts of Wall's and of Kuhn's theories, and showed that when suitably modified in detail Kuhn's model led to the same results as those derived by Wall (Treloar, 1943 a). This modification has been accepted by Kuhn (1946), subject to the reservation referred to earlier on the interpretation of the constant $G$ in terms of molecular quantities. The general stored-energy function (4.9) was obtained by the author (Treloar, 1943 b) by a simple extension of Wall's method; a similar expression representing the entropy in the general strain was published independently by Wall in the same year (Wall, 1943 b). The formula for simple elongation has been derived also by Flory and Rehner (1943) on the basis of a rather different model, and in the same year a detailed account of James and Guth's theory was published (James and Guth, 1943). Both Flory and Rehner and James and Guth included a consideration of swollen rubbers; their conclusions are consistent with the general formula (4.27).

## 7. Appendix

To evaluate the integral

$$\int\!\!\int\!\!\int_{-\infty}^{+\infty} [c - kb^2(x^2 + y^2 + z^2)] e^{-b^2(x^2 + y^2 + z^2)} \, dx \, dy \, dz$$

use is made of the standard forms

$$\int_{-\infty}^{+\infty} e^{-b^2 x^2} \, dx = \pi^{\frac{1}{2}}/b; \qquad \int_{-\infty}^{+\infty} x^2 e^{-b^2 x^2} \, dx = \pi^{\frac{1}{2}}/2b^3,$$

and the terms are arranged in the form of products each involving a single variable.   Thus, for example,

$$\int\int\int_{-\infty}^{+\infty} x^2 e^{-b^2(x^2+y^2+z^2)}\, dx dy dz = \int_{-\infty}^{+\infty} x^2 e^{-b^2 x^2}\, dx \int_{-\infty}^{+\infty} e^{-b^2 y^2}\, dy \int_{-\infty}^{+\infty} e^{-b^2 z^2}\, dz$$

$$= \pi^{\frac{3}{2}}/2b^5.$$

# CHAPTER V

# EXPERIMENTS ON SIMPLE TYPES OF STRAIN

## 1. Form of the stress-strain relations

IN attempting to assess the applicability of the stress-strain relations derived from the statistical theory to actual rubbers, the experimental investigation should not be limited to a single type of strain such as, for example, the commonly employed simple elongation, but should include strains of various types. The simplest types of strain which can be chosen are (1) simple elongation, (2) uni-directional compression or uniform two-dimensional extension, and (3) shear. If it can be shown that the experimental data for all these types of strain may be satisfactorily represented in terms of the general stored-energy function

$$W = \tfrac{1}{2}G(\lambda_1^2 + \lambda_2^2 + \lambda_3^2 - 3) \tag{5.1}$$

and the corresponding stress-strain relations

$$t_1 - t_2 = G(\lambda_1^2 - \lambda_2^2) \tag{5.2}$$

in which only one physical constant $G$ is involved, we may feel more certain that the agreement is genuine than if only a single type of curve had been investigated.

The only experiments which have been reported, dealing with the application of the above three types of strain to identical samples of rubber, were carried out by the author (Treloar, 1944 $a$), who studied vulcanized rubber in (1) simple elongation, (2) uniform two-dimensional extension, and (3) pure shear. These types of strain are represented diagrammatically in Figs. 4.4 ($b$), 4.4 ($c$), and 4.6 ($b$) respectively, the dimensions in the strained state being such as to satisfy the condition of incompressibility. By working with the two-dimensional extension in place of unidirectional compression the difficulties associated with bulging of the sample are avoided, and very much larger strains are possible. Similarly, a large pure shear may be realized much more easily than a large simple shear. Moreover, the types of strain chosen may all be conveniently applied to rubber in the form of sheet, which has the advantage of enabling all the experiments to be performed on a single vulcanized specimen, thus eliminating effects due to possible variations in vulcanizing conditions.

The data here reproduced refer to a natural rubber vulcanized with 8 per cent. of sulphur for 3 hours at 147° C. This rubber

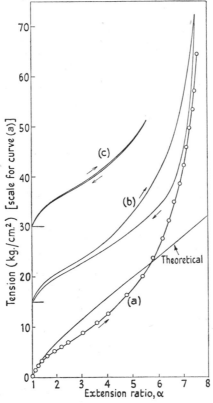

FIG. 5.1. Simple elongation. Comparison of experimental curve with the theoretical form $f = 4 \cdot 0(\alpha - 1/\alpha^2)$.

is rather suitable for the purpose in mind, since it is relatively free from crystallization and hysteresis effects.

*Simple elongation*

Fig. 5.1 shows the behaviour in simple elongation. The curves were obtained by direct loading, with increasing weights applied to the lower clamp at intervals of about 1 minute. Up to about

450 per cent. extension the curves were substantially reversible (curve $c$), but at higher elongations hysteresis effects were apparent. The theoretical curve, equation (4.16 $a$), is fitted to the observed curve ($a$) in the region of small extensions, the required value of $G$ being 4·0 kg./cm.[2] Comparison of these two curves shows the initial curvature of the experimental curve to be rather greater than it should be according to the theory, with the result that the experimental curve falls below the theoretical in the middle region of extension. Finally, at very large extensions, the experimental curve rises more and more rapidly as the breaking-point is approached. This final upward curvature is a consequence of the approach of the network to its limiting extension, in which region the Gaussian formulae become inapplicable.

### Uniform two-dimensional extension

This type of strain was obtained by the inflation of a circular rubber sheet clamped round its circumference, after the manner employed by Flint and Naunton (1937) in their well-known bursting test for rubber sheet, and discussed in more detail by the author (Treloar, 1944 $b$). The strain in the sheet is of course not uniform over its surface, but it is very nearly uniform over a region in the neighbourhood of the centre of the sheet or pole of the spheroidal balloon, to which the measurements were confined. The measurement of the principal extension ratio $\lambda$ in the plane of the sheet may be obtained by observing the displacement of two marked points on its surface. In addition it is necessary to know the radius of curvature $r$ in the polar region (obtained by observations with a travelling microscope) and the gas-pressure $P$. The tensile force $f$ acting across a plane section of the sheet of length 1 cm. is then given by

$$P = 2f/r. \tag{5.3}$$

In plotting the data, as in Fig. 5.2, the abscissae are the extension ratios $\lambda$ in the plane of the sheet, and the ordinates $f/d_0$, where $d_0$ is its original thickness. By equation (4.17 $a$) this should have the form

$$f/d_0 = G(1-1/\lambda^6). \tag{5.4}$$

The experimental points follow this theoretical curve fairly closely up to about $\lambda = 3$, beyond which point the effect of the limited extensibility of the network becomes apparent. It is satisfactory to note that the value of the parameter $G$ which

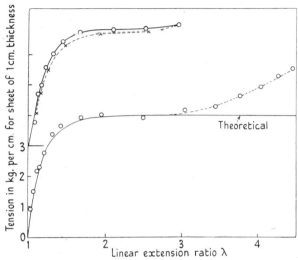

FIG. 5.2. Two-dimensional extension. Comparison of experimental curve with the theoretical form $f/d_0 = 4 \cdot 0(1 - 1/\lambda^6)$.

most nearly represents these experimental results is the same as that chosen to fit the first part of the curve for simple elongation.

*Unidirectional compression*

By the superposition of a suitable hydrostatic pressure, the experimental data for the two-dimensional extension may readily be used to derive the equivalent compressive force corresponding to the same strain. The required pressure is clearly numerically equal to the outwardly directed tensile stress shown in Fig. 4.4 (c). Since the thickness of the strained sheet is $d_0/\lambda^2$, this pressure is $f\lambda^2/d_0$. This is the value of the required compressive *stress*, referred to the strained dimensions. The compressive force $f_c$ referred to the original surface area is obtained by multiplying this stress by the surface area in the strained state, namely $\lambda^2$, so that

$$f_c = f\lambda^4/d_0. \tag{5.5}$$

It is easy to verify the consistency of the theoretical formulae for two-dimensional extension and compression, respectively, when subject to this transformation. For multiplication of the

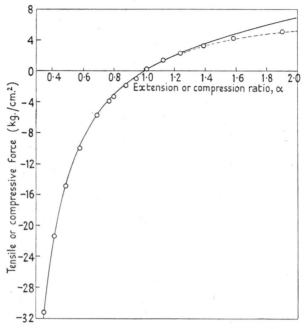

Fig. 5.3. Complete extension and compression curve. The solid line represents the theoretical relation $f = 4\cdot 0(\alpha - 1/\alpha^2)$.

right-hand side of (5.4) by $\lambda^4$ gives for the equivalent compressive force

$$f_c = G(\lambda^4 - 1/\lambda^2); \qquad (5.6)$$

which, with $1/\sqrt{\alpha}$ substituted for $\lambda$, is seen to be identical with equation (4.16 a) except for the sign, which is reversed in the case of a compressive force. Points taken from the two-dimensional compression experiment and converted to equivalent compressive force by means of equation (5.5) are plotted in Fig. 5.3 together with the first part of the simple elongation curve of Fig. 5.1 in order to show the way in which both the elongation and compression points lie on a single curve, with no discontinuity in passing through the origin.

*Pure shear*

From the definition of pure shear (p. 73) it is seen that in this type of strain one dimension remains unchanged in length. A pure shear may therefore be produced by stretching a strip of rubber in such a way that its width remains unchanged. If its

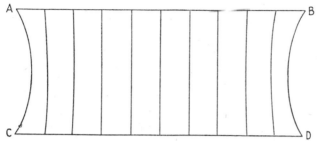

Fig. 5.4. Illustrating distribution of strain on stretching wide sheet. The edges $AB$ and $CD$ are clamped.

length is increased in the ratio $\alpha$, the incompressibility condition then requires that its thickness should diminish in the ratio $1/\alpha$.

Experimentally, a close approximation to pure shear is simply obtained by stretching a short wide strip clamped along the edges $AB$ and $CD$ (Fig. 5.4). If the width is large compared with the length, the non-uniformity of strain is relatively slight, and is limited to a small outer region. This is illustrated by Fig. 5.4, representing the appearance of equally spaced vertical lines in a strip of rubber of 'width' 75 mm. and 'length' 5 mm., stretched to about six times its original length.

Measurement of the stretching force $f$ as a function of the principal extension ratio $\alpha$ for such a strip, by the same method as that used in the simple elongation experiment, resulted in the stress-strain relation shown in Fig. 5.5. The theoretical form (4.19 a), with $G = 4{\cdot}0$, is shown for comparison. Both the theoretical and experimental relations are very similar to the simple elongation curves, though the departure of the experimental curve from the theoretical form is slightly less.

*Simple shear*

To obtain the shear stress $t_{xy}$ corresponding to simple shear of amount $\sigma$ from the tensile force $f$ in a pure shear, use is made of the work of deformation $W$. For, in the case of simple shear, the whole of the work is done by the shearing stress, and hence,

$$t_{xy} = dW/d\sigma,$$

while, in the pure shear, the whole of the work is done by the tensile force $f$, and therefore

$$f = dW/d\alpha.$$

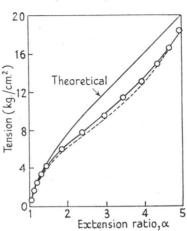

FIG. 5.5. Force-extension relation for wide sheet (pure shear). The theoretical curve has the form $f = 4{\cdot}0(\alpha - 1/\alpha^3)$.

From these two relations it follows that

$$t_{xy} = f(d\alpha/d\sigma).$$

Making use of the relation between the amount of shear $\sigma$ and the principal strain $\alpha$ (eqn. 4.18$b$), we obtain

$$d\alpha/d\sigma = 1/(1+1/\alpha^2),$$

and hence $\qquad t_{xy} = f/(1+1/\alpha^2).$ \hfill (5.7)

The values of $t_{xy}$ derived from the experimental data for pure shear represented in Fig. 5.5 are reproduced in Fig. 5.6. At small strains the curve approximates to the linear form predicted by the theory, but at larger strains an appreciable curvature is evident. The 'modulus of rigidity' corresponding to the initial portion of the curve has the value $4{\cdot}0$ kg./cm.$^2$

An alternative method of representing the data of Figs. 5.1,

5.2, and 5.5, which provides a more direct comparison between the various types of strain, is based on equation (5.2), according to which the difference between any two of the three principal stresses should be proportional to the difference of the squares of the corresponding extension ratios. For a simple elongation

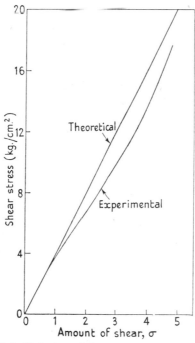

FIG. 5.6. Relation of shear stress to shear strain calculated from data of Fig. 5.5. The slope of the theoretical line is 4·0 kg./cm.²

the stress calculated on the original section is $\alpha f$, where $f$ is the force referred to the original cross-section. Hence, if $t_1$ is the stress corresponding to the force $f$, we have $t_2 = t_3 = 0$, and therefore $t_1 - t_2 = \alpha f$. The corresponding difference of the squares of the extension ratios, $\lambda_1^2 - \lambda_2^2$, is equal to $\alpha^2 - 1/\alpha$. Plotting $t_1 - t_2$ against $\lambda_1^2 - \lambda_2^2$ then yields the curve shown in Fig. 5.7. The remaining curves for pure shear and two-dimensional extension are obtained in a similar way. If equation (5.2) applied exactly all these data would fall on a single straight line; actually they fall on divergent curves, showing that the theoretical law becomes inaccurate at large strains.

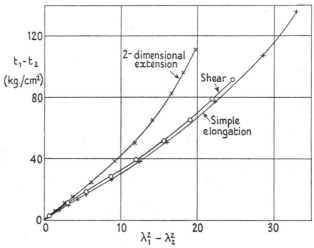

Fig. 5.7. Alternative representation of data given in Figs. 5.1, 5.2, and 5.5.

## 2. General conclusion

The conclusion to be drawn from these experiments is that the formulae of the statistical theory, involving a single physical constant, correctly describe the properties of a real rubber to a first approximation. In particular, they provide a basis for the understanding of the relation between the stress-strain curves for different types of strain. However, in view of the very general nature of the theoretical arguments, and the simplifications introduced in the treatment of the network model, it is not surprising to find deviations from the ideal theoretical behaviour. These deviations, which appear not to be limited to the particular type of rubber here examined, are of two kinds. Firstly, at moderate strains, there is a tendency for the stresses to fall below the theoretical values, and secondly, at very large strains, the stresses tend to rise and may eventually greatly exceed the theoretical values. The second of these effects is understood in principle; it arises from the finite extensibility of the network, and may be taken into account by a more complete statistical theory, as will be shown in a later chapter. The first effect is not at all well understood. In a series of experiments on the effect of swelling on the shape of the stress-strain curve in simple elongation, Gee (1946) finds the departure from the theoretical form to become progressively reduced as the swelling is increased. His tentative explanation of the discrepancy is that the chains do not exist in their ideally random configurations, but are arranged in some locally ordered or alined manner with respect to one another. A local order of this kind, less extended and perhaps less perfect than that found in the crystalline state, might correspond to a more favourable state of 'packing' of the molecules than a completely random arrangement, and would naturally have an effect on the entropy of the network which would be different in the strained and unstrained states, respectively. Swelling would be expected to reduce the tendency to alinement, and should thus lead to a closer approach to the ideal behaviour.

Gee's observations on the effect of swelling are to some extent borne out by some later experiments by the author dealing with the most general homogeneous strain in dry and swollen rubbers, though in these experiments the swelling failed to remove the deviations from the ideal behaviour entirely. A fuller discussion of these experiments will be given later, when the question of departures from the ideal statistical theory will be examined (Chap. VII). In the present chapter the intention is rather to point out the general agreement between the theoretical and experimental behaviour than to investigate the relatively small discrepancies.

## 3. Theoretical derivation of the modulus

The quantity $G$ in the general stress-strain relation (5.2) has, in the section above, been treated as an arbitrary parameter. In reality, however, $G$ is determined by the structure of the network, and on the simple assumption that the chains have an initial distribution of lengths corresponding to that for free chains, the statistical theory leads to the result (cf. p. 66)

$$G = NkT = \rho RT/M_c, \tag{5.8}$$

where $N$ is the number of chains, and $M_c$ is their mean weight.

Experimental verification of this relation in an exact quantitative manner is a matter of considerable difficulty, because there is no known way of introducing a precisely determined number of cross-linkages between the molecules. The most careful work on this aspect of the problem has been carried out by Flory (1946), who used a series of butyl rubbers, in which

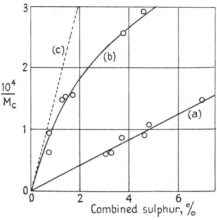

Fig. 5.8. Dependence of cross-linking on sulphur content. (Gee, 1947.)
(a) Rubber-sulphur compounds. (b) Accelerated compounds. (c) Theoretical.

the degree of cross-linking was estimated by an indirect method. Additional data, of relative rather than absolute significance, have been obtained by Gee (1947a), working with natural rubber.

In Gee's experiments the modulus $G$ was measured on a number of rubber vulcanizates swollen in petrol. Several types of compound were used. The first series contained rubber and sulphur only, other series included accelerators of various kinds in addition to rubber and sulphur. The degree of cross-linking was varied by suitable variations in the proportion of added sulphur and accelerator, or by variation in the time or temperature of curing. Typical results are shown in Fig. 5.8. The rubber-sulphur compounds yielded a linear relation between $1/M_c$, calculated from equation (5.8), and the amount of combined sulphur. The theoretical line corresponding to the formation of one cross-link for each sulphur atom chemically combined with the rubber (curve c) has a much higher slope. In fact, the experiments of Bloomfield (1946) and of Farmer and Shipley (1946) on the reaction of low-molecular polyisoprenes with sulphur show the presence of linkages containing 2, 4, or 6 sulphur atoms. In addition, some sulphur is combined in a non-cross-linking or cyclic manner. As a result, the average number of sulphur atoms per cross-linkage was found to range from 4 to 8, according to the particular hydrocarbon investigated. The factor of about 8 which Gee finds it necessary to introduce in order to bring his experimental line into agreement with the theoretical line based on monosulphide linkages is therefore entirely reasonable. With accelerated compounds, on the other hand, the number of cross-links was not proportional to the sulphur content (Fig. 5.8 (b)). In the particular case of T.M.T. compounds, cross-linking was effected without appreciable combination of sulphur, presumably through direct C—C linkages. In accelerated compounds, therefore, it is clear that the amount of combined sulphur is not proportional to the degree of cross-linking, which varies with the type of accelerator and with the conditions of vulcanization.

In Flory's experiments with butyl rubbers an attempt was made to determine the degree of cross-linking by an independent method. Butyl rubber is essentially polyisobutylene

$$[-C(CH_3)_2-CH_2-]_n$$

incorporating a small percentage of a conjugated diene (isoprene or butadiene) in order to provide the double bonds necessary for cross-linkage or vulcanization. Unfortunately only a fraction of the double bonds normally take part in the cross-linking reaction, hence an indirect method must be used to determine the number of cross-links. The procedure adopted by Flory was as follows. A given (unvulcanized) butyl rubber was first separated into a number of fractions of different average molecular weight, each of which possessed the same percentage of a diolefin, and hence the same potential cross-linking capacity. The fractions were vulcanized under standard conditions, so that the number of cross-links per unit volume was the same in each. They were then treated with a solvent to remove any fraction of the molecules not attached to the network structure. Obviously the proportion of such soluble constituents is a function of the molecular weight of the unvulcanized rubber. For rubbers of high molecular weight it is negligible; but as the molecular weight is reduced it increases,

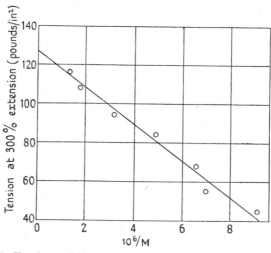

FIG. 5.9. Tension at 300 per cent. elongation v. reciprocal molecular weight ($M$) before vulcanization. (Flory, 1946.)

finally becoming 100 per cent. at a critical molecular weight $M'$, known as the 'gel point'. This critical point was not actually reached, but was estimated by extrapolation of the curve relating percentage 'sol' with molecular weight.

To obtain the number of cross-links Flory makes use of the theory of random cross-linking, which shows that for molecules of uniform length the gel point corresponds to a number of cross-links equal to half the number of original molecules. It follows that $M_c$, the average chain length, is equal to $M'$.

Fig. 5.9 is a typical example chosen from Flory's data for the variation of tension at an extension ratio of 4·0 (which is proportional to $G$) with initial molecular weight, for a series of otherwise identical vulcanized rubbers, for which, therefore, both $M_c$ and $\nu_0$ in equation (4.13) are constant. The form of the dependence on $M$ agrees extremely well with the theoretical prediction, for values of $M$ ranging from 114,000 to 730,000. The slope of the line in Fig. 5.9 gives for the value of $M_c$ a figure of 37,000, which compares favourably with the value of 35,000 calculated from the gel point. Thus the general validity of Flory's analysis is well established.

The variation of the tension with degree of cross-linking does not conform so well with expectations. Using the experimentally determined values of $M_c$, the values of $G$ for three differently cross-linked rubbers calculated from the formula (4.14), with $g = 1$, were 35, 50, and 58 lb. per square inch, whilst the observed values were respectively 127, 135, and 145. In other words, the factor $g$ varied from 3·6 for the lowest degree of cross-linking to 2·5 for the highest, suggesting that the effect of entanglements and other network defects becomes reduced as the chain length is reduced, as appears not unreasonable from general considerations. However, it is by no means certain that the factor obtained by Flory should be wholly attributed to network defects of the kind which he envisages. The problem is evidently a difficult one, in which various sources of uncertainty are likely to be present. It has already been pointed out in Chapter III that a factor of about 2·3 was introduced by Kuhn for quite different reasons, namely interferences due to the presence of junction points in the vicinity of a given chain. Also, the further analysis of the network problem by James and Guth (1947) suggests a modification of the theoretical value of the constant $G$ which would have the effect of increasing the discrepancy between theory and experiment to a factor of about 4. On the experimental side, also, difficulties arise in the measurement of the stresses. From Chapter II it is clear that stresses measured at a rather rapid rate must differ considerably from equilibrium stresses, and this difference might well be a function of the degree of cross-linking. It must be noted, too, that the measurement of the stress at 300 per cent. elongation is not ideal, since as Flory's curves show, this is already in the non-Gaussian region, where the simple statistical formulae do not apply accurately. For these reasons the question of the quantitative dependence of $G$ on $M_c$ cannot be regarded as conclusively settled. The importance of these pioneer investigations probably lies rather in the fact that here, for the first time, definite proof is given that the modulus varies with degree of cross-linking in the manner predicted by the statistical theory, while its absolute value is of the correct order of magnitude. The discrepancy between theory and experiment is probably not unreasonable, in view of the uncertainties inherent in the experimental approach, as well as in the theoretical analysis.

# CHAPTER VI

# REFINEMENTS TO THE THEORY IN THE REGION OF VERY LARGE STRAINS

## 1. Introduction

UP to this point the development of the statistical theory of the network has been specifically limited to the region of small and moderately large strains, in which the Gaussian formula for the distribution of displacement lengths, and the corresponding linear force-extension relation for the individual chain, may be considered to be valid approximations. In Chapter III it was pointed out that in practice this limitation involves no difficulty so long as the molecular extension amounts to no more than one-third of the maximum extended length, but for higher extensions the Gaussian approximation becomes increasingly inadequate as the extension is increased towards its limiting value. Similar considerations limit the range of applicability of the formulae for the stored energy and the resultant stress-strain relations derived in Chapter IV, all of which rest on the same assumption of a Gaussian distribution of displacement lengths. As a result, these formulae cease to represent the behaviour of real rubbers in the region of very large strains, i.e. strains approaching the maximum strains which can be applied. This has already been noticed in comparing the experimental stress-strain curves with the corresponding Gaussian formulae in the last chapter, and is particularly apparent, for example, in the case of simple elongation (Fig. 5.1).

This deficiency has been dealt with by introducing suitable refinements into the statistical theory, some of which will be considered in the following pages. Since the subject is essentially a mathematical one, it will be necessary to omit detailed proofs of the results and to content ourselves with an outline of the methods of approach, and with the more important conclusions.

## 2. Statistical treatment of the random chain

*The inverse Langevin approximation*

As in the elementary statistical theory of the single chain

dealt with in Chapter III, so also in the more accurate treatment, it is convenient to replace the actual molecular structure by an idealized random chain, in which the direction in space of any particular link is entirely random and independent of that of neighbouring links in the chain. If such a chain is represented by $n$ links each of length $l$, we have to find the probability that the end $B$ (Fig. 3.5) shall be within a small volume element $d\tau$ at a distance $r$ from the end $A$.

In the method of dealing with this problem adopted by W. Kuhn and his associates it is necessary first to find the *distribution in angle* of the individual links of the chain when its ends are fixed at the two points $A$ and $B$. This problem has a precise meaning only if the number of links is large; the system may then be treated as a statistical assembly of links, and although each link is subject to continual fluctuations, the system as a whole will settle down into a steady state in which the proportion of links at any particular angle remains essentially constant.

The method of solution of this problem given by W. Kuhn and Grün (1942) follows lines which are familiar in statistical thermodynamics. They consider first a particular distribution in which the number of links included in any given range of angle ($d\theta_i$) with respect to the direction of the vector $AB$ is arbitrarily chosen (say $n_i$). If the *a priori* probability that a particular link should have a particular direction is known, it is then possible to write down the probability $W_i$ of this particular distribution. The distribution actually established will be that distribution for which the calculated probability has a maximum value. This most probable distribution may be found by an extension of the usual method of finding the turning-point of a function; it involves finding the condition that the value of the probability $W_i$ is unaffected by small variations in all the chosen $n_i$, subject, of course, to the necessary restricting conditions of the stated problem (e.g. that the ends of the chain are fixed in position). The solution obtained by this method is expressed by the following formula for the number of links $dn$ in the range of angle $d\theta$;

$$dn = (n\beta/\sinh\beta)e^{\beta\cos\theta}\tfrac{1}{2}\sin\theta\,d\theta. \qquad (6.1)$$

It will be seen to involve one parameter $\beta$, which is itself determined by the fractional extension of the chain $(r/nl)$, thus

$$r/nl = \coth\beta - 1/\beta = \mathscr{L}(\beta), \qquad (6.1\,a)$$

where $\mathscr{L}$ is known as the Langevin function. Alternatively we may write

$$\beta = \mathscr{L}^{-1}(r/nl), \qquad (6.1\,b)$$

where $\mathscr{L}^{-1}$ is the corresponding inverse Langevin function.

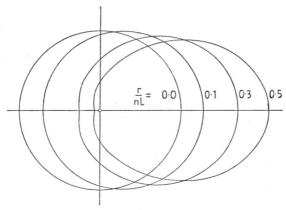

FIG. 6.1. Angular distribution of links in random chain.
(W. Kuhn and Grün, 1942.) Parameter, $r/nl$.

The distribution of link angles represented by (6.1) is thus determined only by the fractional extension $(r/nl)$, and is therefore independent of $n$, the number of links in the chain. In order to appreciate its significance, it may conveniently be represented graphically, as has been done by W. Kuhn and Grün. For this purpose a polar diagram is most suitable. The vector $r$ (Fig. 6.1) in such a diagram is made proportional to the probability of an angle $\theta$. (In this plot the factor $\frac{1}{2}\sin\theta$ is omitted; this is a purely geometrical factor representing the element of area on the surface of a sphere corresponding to the angular range $d\theta$.) It will be noticed that if $r/nl = 0$ the distribution in angle is uniform, as in the unrestricted chain, and that with increasing separation of the chain ends the distribution becomes more and more asymmetrical.

The probability of a given vector length $r$ for the chain follows immediately from the distribution of link angles. For the probability of a length $r$ is simply proportional to the probability of the most probable distribution of link angles corresponding to the length $r$. The required *probability density* $p(r)$ is most conveniently represented in a logarithmic form, as below,

$$\ln p(r) = \text{const.} - n\left[\frac{r}{nl}\beta + \ln\frac{\beta}{\sinh\beta}\right],\qquad(6.2)$$

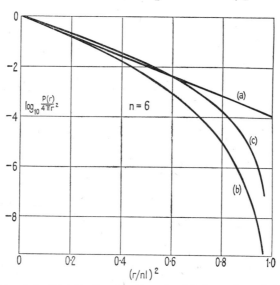

Fig. 6.2. Distribution functions for 6-link random chain. (a) Gaussian approximation. (b) Langevin approximation (eqn. 6.2). (c) Accurate (eqn. 6.5).

which is equivalent to the formula of W. Kuhn and H. Kuhn (1946). Alternatively this expression may be expanded into the form of the following series:

$$\ln p(r) = \text{const.} - n\left[\frac{3}{2}\left(\frac{r}{nl}\right)^2 + \frac{9}{20}\left(\frac{r}{nl}\right)^4 + \frac{99}{350}\left(\frac{r}{nl}\right)^6 + \ldots\right].$$

$$(6.2\,a)$$

The Gaussian formula (eqn. 3.7) gives

$$\ln p(r) = \text{const.} - 3r^2/2nl^2,\qquad(6.2\,b)$$

corresponding to the first term only of this series. This is adequate so long as the terms in $(r/nl)^4$, etc., are small, i.e. so long as $\frac{3}{10}(r/nl)^2$ is small compared with unity. Thus if $r/nl$ is $\frac{1}{3}$, the error in $\ln p(r)$ involved in the Gaussian approximation is only about 3 per cent., while if $r/nl$ is $\frac{1}{2}$, the error is about 8 per cent. At still larger extensions the Gaussian formula ceases to be a useful approximation.

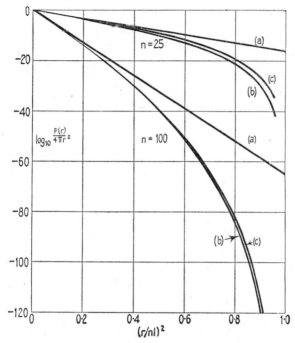

Fig. 6.3. Distribution functions for 25- and 100-link random chains.
(a) Gaussian approximation. (b) Langevin approximation (eqn. 6.2.)
(c) Accurate (eqn. 6.5).

The probability $P(r)\,dr$ of a length lying between $r$ and $r+dr$, irrespective of direction, is obtained exactly as in the Gaussian case (Chap. III) by multiplying the probability density (given by (6.2)) by the size of the volume element, which in this case is $4\pi r^2\,dr$. The form of the function (6.2) is shown in the accompanying Figs. 6.2 and 6.3. The approach to the Gaussian form when $r/nl$ is small is clearly shown, as is also the approach to an asymptotic limit at the maximum extension of the chain ($r/nl = 1$), where the probability falls to zero.

As in Chapter III, the entropy $s$ of the single chain may be taken as proportional to the logarithm of the probability density as given by (6.2). Hence

$$s = c_2 - kn\left[\frac{r}{nl}\beta + \ln\frac{\beta}{\sinh\beta}\right], \qquad (6.3)$$

where, as before, $\qquad \beta = \mathscr{L}^{-1}(r/nl).$

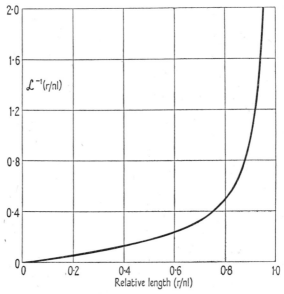

FIG. 6.4. The complete force-extension relation for a random chain.

The tension on the chain when its ends are held at a distance $r$ apart is $-T\,ds/dr$ (cf. eqn. 3.14), which is

$$f = (kT/l)\mathscr{L}^{-1}(r/nl). \qquad (6.4)$$

The function $\mathscr{L}^{-1}(r/nl)$ may be expanded into the following series:

$$\mathscr{L}^{-1}\!\left(\frac{r}{nl}\right) = 3\!\left(\frac{r}{nl}\right) + \frac{9}{5}\!\left(\frac{r}{nl}\right)^3 + \frac{297}{175}\!\left(\frac{r}{nl}\right)^5 + \dots, \qquad (6.4\,a)$$

from which it is seen that if $r/nl$ is not greater than about $\frac{1}{3}$ the terms involving powers of $r/nl$ higher than the first may be neglected. In this region the force-extension relation reduces to the linear form, corresponding to the Gaussian distribution.

The complete force-extension relation over the whole range from $r/nl = 0$ to $r/nl = 1$, represented by the inverse Langevin function (6.4), is illustrated in Fig. 6.4. This form has been obtained by James and Guth (1943) as well as by W. Kuhn and H. Kuhn (1946).

### The series distribution formula

There is one general criticism of some importance which may be raised in connexion with the above treatment of the statistical problem of the random chain. This treatment rests upon methods which are standard practice in statistical thermodynamics, but which are in principle valid only for systems containing a very large number of elements. In dealing with molecular systems, for example, it is customary to think in terms of volumes containing numbers of the order of $10^{23}$ molecules, which is of course entirely adequate for treatment by the usual statistical methods. But in the problem with which we are concerned, namely the randomly kinked chain, the condition that the number of elements (i.e. links) should be large is by no means obviously fulfilled. As we shall see later, the number of links in an average random chain corresponding to vulcanized rubber may be of the order 100. The question arises whether 100 is a sufficiently large number for the methods of statistical thermodynamics to be applied.

There appears to be no direct way of answering this question. Indirectly, however, it is possible to provide an answer by working out the solution to the random chain problem by an independent and more accurate method, and comparing the result with that derived above.

The alternative method treats the problem as a purely geometrical question and introduces no approximations of any kind; the result is therefore accurate for chains of any number of links, from 1 upwards. This solution was obtained by the author (Treloar, 1946 a) by a simple transformation of a result obtained many years earlier by Hall (1927) and Irwin (1927) in connexion with the theory of random sampling. For a chain of $n$ links, each of length $l$, the probability of an end-to-end distance between $r$ and $r+dr$ (irrespective of direction) is represented by the formula

$$P(r)\,dr = \frac{r}{2l^2}\frac{n^{n-2}}{(n-2)!}\sum_{s=0}^{k}(-1)^s\binom{n}{s}(m-s/n)^{n-2}\,dr,\quad (6.5)$$

where    $k/n \leqslant m \leqslant (k+1)/n$    and    $m = \tfrac{1}{2}(1-r/nl)$

and $\binom{n}{s}$ represents the number of combinations of $n$ things taken $s$ at a time.

Distribution curves for three different chain lengths, corresponding to $n = 6$, 25, and 100 respectively, calculated from this formula, are represented in Figs. 6.2 and 6.3. The quantity plotted is the probability density $P(r)/4\pi r^2$, so that the curves may be compared with those discussed in the previous section, and an arbitrary constant is added so that all the curves start from the origin. It will be seen that the curves are not all of the same form, i.e. the probability represented by equation (6.5) is not determined only by the ratio $r/nl$, as it was in the less accurate function (6.2). Comparison of the respective curves shows that for $n = 6$ (Fig. 6.2) the inverse Langevin approximation, though very much better than the Gaussian form, is quantitatively seriously in error. At $n = 25$, however, the difference between the two formulae is already quite small, while at $n = 100$ it has become entirely negligible (Fig. 6.3).

The conclusion to be drawn from these calculations is that for chain lengths of the order with which we are concerned in rubbers the Langevin approximation is likely to be sufficiently accurate for practical purposes, and is clearly preferable to the accurate but more cumbersome series formula (6.5).

## 3. Application to real molecules

While there is no doubt that the formulae (6.2), (6.3), and (6.4) represent a considerable advance on the corresponding Gaussian approximations, there still remains the rather formidable difficulty of relating any particular real molecular structure to the mathematically idealized random chain. There is no a priori reason for the assumption (introduced by W. Kuhn) that any real molecule may be regarded as statistically equivalent to the random chain over the whole range of extension, if a suitable choice is made of the number of bonds in the real chain to be equated to one link of the random chain.

Some light is thrown on this relationship by another quite different method of treatment which was developed by the author before the general solution of the random chain problem had become available. In principle this method could be applied to any type of chain structure; actually, it was applied to two representative structures, the paraffin or polyethylene chain (Treloar, 1943 c), and the rubber or polyisoprene chain (Treloar, 1944 c). The method makes use of a type of graphical computation, which is able to deal with the particular arrangement of bond lengths and valence angles for comparatively short chains (e.g. five C—C bonds in the case of the paraffin molecule). Longer chains are then 'built up' by combining these short chains in a purely random manner, that is, without regard to valence angle considerations. In these calculations the single bond angle was given its usual value ($109\frac{1}{2}°$), while the single-double bond angle in polyisoprene was taken as $125·25°$. The values assumed for the single and double bond lengths were $1·54$ and $1·34$ Angstrom units, respectively. Complete freedom of rotation was assumed for single-single bond junctions, and complete rigidity for single-double bond junctions.

A check on the accuracy of this method of derivation of the distribution functions, and on the error introduced by neglecting the valence angle in joining up the lower-membered chains, was provided by comparing the resulting root-mean-square values of $r$ with those given by the formulae of Eyring or Wall (Chap. III). Representative sets of data chosen from the published results are reproduced in Fig. 6.5, in which (a) refers to the 80-link paraffin chain and (b) to the rubber chain containing 64 isoprene units. The comparison curves represent distributions for random chains, derived from the formula (6.2), the value of $n$, the number of links in the corresponding random chain, being adjusted to give the best fit in each case. In view of the fact that the methods are entirely independent, the agreement in form is rather striking. The 64-isoprene chain appears to correspond almost exactly with the 90-link random chain, so that *a long polyisoprene chain may be considered to be statistically equivalent over the whole range of extension to a random*

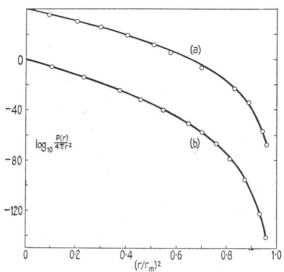

FIG. 6.5. Comparison of paraffin and polyisoprene chains with random chains. (*a*) Circles, 80-link paraffin; continuous curve, 34-link random. (*b*) Circles, 64-isoprene; continuous curve, 90-link random.

*chain in which there are 1·4 freely jointed links for each isoprene unit.*

For the paraffin chain the fit is not quite so good, and it may be that this structure is not identical (statistically) with a random chain. However, in view of the slight inaccuracies involved in the calculations, the difference is too small to be regarded as definitely established. In any case it is not large enough to be practically significant. We may therefore say that approximately, the paraffin chain is equivalent to a random chain containing one link for each 2·35 links of the paraffin chain.

*Limitations of the foregoing treatment*

For the particular structures considered above, the assumption of an equivalent random chain is thus proved to be very near the truth. Before leaving this question, however, it is necessary to emphasize again that in these statistical treatments the chains are regarded as purely geometrical structures, and all effects of the volume occupied by the atoms, or of the forces between atoms, are specifically excluded from consideration. We have already seen in Chapter III that the presence of an energy barrier to rotation about bonds may considerably affect the statistical length of a chain. In neglecting these effects, therefore, the present treatment is obviously very much over-simplified, and the results may well be quantitatively inaccurate, though their general form is probably not seriously in error on this account. Indeed, there is some experimental evidence that the average extension of rubber-like molecules in solution is definitely greater than the theory of random kinking, as here presented, would require. The most important information of this kind has been provided by W. Kuhn and H. Kuhn (1943) on the basis of experimental data for the birefringence of flow of solutions of long-chain molecules, a property which is rather sensitive to the molecular dimensions. Taking these data in conjunction with viscosity data for the same solutions, it is possible, by means of the theory worked out by W. Kuhn and H. Kuhn, to estimate the degree of kinking of the polymer molecule, or, what amounts to the same thing, the number of links in the equivalent random chain. This method confirms the expected differences between relatively stiff molecules like cellulose and the flexible molecules of typical rubbers. Thus, for example, for cellulose, the length of the 'equivalent statistical element' or link of the equivalent random chain is found to be 50 Angstrom units, while for natural rubber it is only 13 A., and for paraffins (in chloroform) 16 A. The value for rubber corresponds to 2·8 isoprene units per random link. This is about four times the author's theoretical value (0·71). Since the average extension of the chain is proportional to the square root of the number of links, a difference of this amount would mean that the actual chain has about twice the average length (in the unstressed state) calculated theoretically. This difference might very well be due mainly to the effect of the volume occupied by the atoms.

For paraffin chains W. Kuhn and H. Kuhn's value corresponds to 12·6 C—C bonds per random link. This has to be compared with the theoretical figure of 2·35. The factor here is slightly larger ($\sim$ 5), possibly because, in addition to the volume-filling effect, there is an inherent stiffness (of the kind discussed in Chapter III) tending to preserve the planar zigzag form.

## 4. Bond stretching and valence angle distortion

The preceding statistical analyses involve the implicit assumption that the bond lengths and valence angles are not substantially affected by the application of a tensile force. This obviously cannot be strictly true, and a theoretical analysis designed to include a correction for these bond distortion effects has been carried out by W. Kuhn and H. Kuhn (1946). These effects can only become important at very high stresses, for which the chain is very nearly fully extended. It is therefore permissible to regard the additional extension of the chain due to bond distortions as being identical with the increase in length which would be produced in a fully extended chain by the application of the same force. This additional extension is calculated for the particular case of the polyethylene chain. For this purpose the force constant for bond stretching is obtained from the known vibration frequencies for bonds of this type, while the force constant for valence angle deformation is estimated from a comparison of the heats of combustion of certain ring compounds in which the valence angles are abnormal, and also from information derived from Raman spectra. The total force constant due to the combined effect of bond stretching and valence angle distortion is given by W. Kuhn and H. Kuhn as

$$a = 2 \cdot 5 \times 10^{-3} \text{ dynes,}$$

where $a$ is defined by the relation

$$f = a(\delta L / L),$$

in which $L$ refers to the fully extended length of the unstressed chain or the 'hydrodynamic' length of the chain. This means

that a force of $2 \cdot 5 \times 10^{-5}$ dynes will produce a fractional extension of 1 per cent. on the hydrodynamic length.

The extension of the chain due to these distortions produced
by the force $f$ is then superimposed on the normal extension
due to the configurational entropy effect, which is represented
by an expression of the type of equation (6.4), having the form

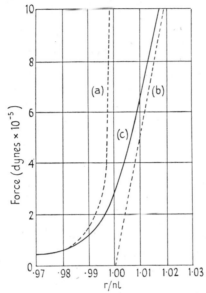

FIG. 6.6. Effect of bond distortion on force-extension relation
for single chain. (W. Kuhn and H. Kuhn, 1946.)

shown in Fig. 6.5. Since this relation applies directly only to
the chain of randomly jointed links, it is necessary to assign
a value to the length $l$ of the equivalent random link. The
value chosen by W. Kuhn and H. Kuhn is $l = 16 . 10^{-8}$ cm.,
based on the experimental evidence discussed above. With this
value of $l$, the entropy force-extension relation, for a temperature of 300° K., calculated from (6.4), is as shown by the broken
line (a) in Fig. 6.6. The extension due to bond distortion is
represented by the straight line relation (b). The total extension, obtained by superimposing (b) on (a), is represented by
the full-line curve (c).

An examination of this diagram shows that the bond-distortion effect becomes appreciable only when the extension exceeds 97 per cent. of the hydrodynamic length. The effect of the correction is to shift the asymptote to the curve from a vertical to a slightly inclined position. The calculations obviously apply only for comparatively small bond distortions, for which the strain may be considered proportional to the stress. If appreciable bond distortion of the kind envisaged does occur, it will give rise to both internal energy and entropy changes on its own account, and the tension will no longer arise simply from an entropy effect. Whether these effects are likely to be of practical significance remains to be seen.

## 5. The network of non-Gaussian chains

### General considerations

The next step in the theoretical development consists in incorporating the more accurate statistical theory of the random chain into the general theory of the network, in other words, the extension of the network theory to the non-Gaussian region. It must be said at once that the problems raised by this extension of the network theory are mathematically and physically very formidable, and none of the proposed solutions can be regarded as resting on the same sure basis as that on which the corresponding Gaussian problem has been established. These reservations apply only to the quantitative aspects of the theory; qualitatively, the principal results derived are undoubtedly genuine.

One of the main difficulties arises from the fact that the more accurate distribution function (6.2), unlike the Gaussian distribution function, does not possess the fortunate property of being decomposable into three component probabilities related to the $x$-, $y$-, and $z$-coordinates separately. Thus, in the Gaussian region, the extension of a chain in (say) the $x$-direction, in no way affects its probable extension in the $y$- or $z$-directions; in the non-Gaussian region this is no longer true, for the component probabilities are no longer independent.

The second main difficulty concerns the distribution of chain displacement lengths in the strained state. In the Gaussian network theory (Chap. IV) it was assumed by W. Kuhn, and proved by James and Guth, that the deformation of chain displacement lengths was proportional to the deformation of corresponding dimensions in the bulk rubber or, stated differently, that the junction points of the network move like particles embedded in an elastic continuum. This assumption cannot apply in the non-Gaussian region, (a) because the force-extension relation for a single chain is non-linear, and (b) because a chain cannot exceed its maximum 'hydrodynamic' length $L$.

### James and Guth's theory

These difficulties, and others associated with them, do not arise suddenly at any particular degree of strain, but are inherent in the whole network problem from the beginning. With small strains, however, they are entirely negligible. At moderate strains, e.g. where the stress-strain relation for simple elongation begins to develop an upward curvature, they begin to become significant, while at very high strains (near the breaking-point) they assume an overriding importance. In James and Guth's (1943) modification of the Gaussian theory they are, in effect, ignored. All the conclusions derived from the Gaussian theory are simply taken over and applied to the non-Gaussian region, with the single difference that the Gaussian force-extension relation for the single chain is replaced by a function of the inverse Langevin type (eqn. 6.4). This is, of course, not a very satisfactory procedure from the mathematical standpoint, as James and Guth realize, but they suggest that it should not be far from the truth, except at the highest strains.

To be more precise, the set of three independent hypothetical Gaussian chains parallel to the coordinate axes to which the Gaussian network is shown to be equivalent is replaced, in James and Guth's modified theory, by a similar set of non-Gaussian chains. The subsequent analysis follows exactly as for the Gaussian network. The resulting stress-strain relation for simple elongation has the form

$$f = \frac{G}{3\kappa}\big[\mathscr{L}^{-1}(\kappa\alpha) - 3\kappa/\alpha^2\big], \tag{6.6}$$

where $f$ is the force (referred to the original cross-sectional area), $\alpha$ is the extension ratio, and $G$ and $\kappa$ are constants. For small values of $\alpha$ the constant $\kappa$ disappears, and the equation reduces to the Gaussian form

$$f = G(\alpha - 1/\alpha^2).$$

The additional constant $\kappa$ is related to the limited extensibility of the real (non-Gaussian) molecules. It is, in fact, equal to the fractional extension of the hypothetical chains in the undeformed state. It follows that $1/\kappa$ measures the extensibility of the chains, and hence of the network.

A typical curve calculated from equation (6.6), using $\kappa = 0 \cdot 1$, is shown in Fig. 6.8. The maximum extension in this case is given by $\alpha = 10$. It is clear that the general shape of this curve corresponds much more closely in the high-extension region with the stress-strain curves for actual rubbers (Fig. 5.1) than does the original Gaussian formula.

Although in the formula (6.6) the two constants $G$ and $\kappa$ appear as independent parameters, they are in fact mutually related. For $G$ is determined by the number of chains per unit volume, while $\kappa$ is a function of the length of the chains. This relationship will appear more clearly after the author's alternative theoretical treatment has been considered.

### The author's theory

A method of treatment which takes into account some of the factors omitted from James and Guth's theory, and which partly meets the two main difficulties referred to in the earlier section, has been put forward by the author. Essentially it is based on the principle proposed by Flory and Rehner (1943) and successfully applied by them to the Gaussian network problem.

The method consists in calculating the entropy of deformation of a small 'cell' or element of the network which may conveniently consist of four chains radiating outwards from a common junction point (Fig. 6.7). If the chains all have the same contour length, the average positions of their outer ends, or nearest neighbour junction points, will be at the four corners of a regular tetrahedron. It is now assumed that the properties of the bulk rubber may be correctly represented by the properties of this elementary cell of the network.

In the calculation of the entropy the outer junction points *ABCD* are considered fixed, while the central junction point is permitted to fluctuate in position in response to the random motion of the attached chains. It is necessary to calculate the probability that the four chains, fixed at their outer extremities, should meet within a small volume element in the neighbourhood of some arbitrarily chosen point *P*. The probability of their meeting at any place is then obtained by integrating this particular probability over all space. If this integration

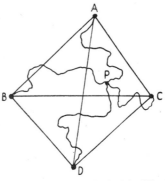

FIG. 6.7. The tetrahedral 'cell' of Flory and Rehner (1943).

is carried out first with the unstrained tetrahedron, and then with the tetrahedron subjected to an 'affine deformation' corresponding to the strain applied to the rubber, the second probability is found to be smaller than the first. The ratio of the two probabilities gives the entropy of deformation.

The application of this method to non-Gaussian chains involves no new principle. It is only necessary to substitute the more accurate distribution function for the chain displacement lengths for the Gaussian formula used by Flory and Rehner. The calculations were made by the author for two different chain lengths, represented by $n = 25$ and $n = 100$ respectively. The series formula (6.5) was actually used for the chain probabilities, but for these values of $n$ the results would not have been significantly different if the inverse Langevin approximation (6.2) had been substituted for this. In either case, the formulae are too complicated to be handled in general terms, and the calculations have to proceed on a numerical basis.

The stress-strain curves for simple elongation calculated in this way are shown in Fig. 6.8. They show clearly the gradual departure from the Gaussian form with increasing extension. The maximum extension is proportional to the square root of the number of links in the chain. The extensibility of the network, however, is somewhat greater (on this model) than the extensibility of the chains of which it is composed. A 100-link chain may be extended to 10 times its average length in the

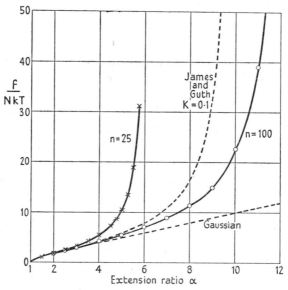

Fig. 6.8. Theoretical force-extension curves for network of non-Gaussian chains.

unstressed state. For such a chain James and Guth's formula gives the curve shown dotted in Fig. 6.8; on the author's theory the extensibility is about 25 per cent. higher.

The vertical scale in Fig. 6.8 gives $f/NkT$. To determine the absolute value of the stress it is necessary to know $N$, the number of chains per unit volume of the network, or alternatively, the molecular weight of the chain, $M_c$. The molecular weight to be assigned to a random chain depends, of course, on the nature of the molecule which the random chain is taken to represent. For isoprene rubber the author adopted the theoretical figure of 1·4 random links as the statistical equivalent of one isoprene unit. On this basis the 100-link random chain corresponds to a rubber chain comprising 71 isoprene units, and having, therefore, a molecular weight of 4,800, while the 25-link random chain corresponds to a molecular weight of 1,200. With these figures, the absolute stress-strain relations take the form shown in Fig. 6.9.

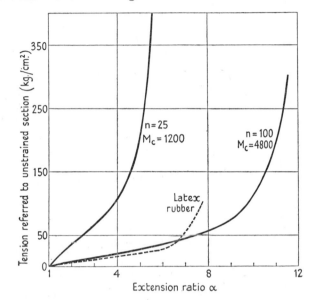

FIG. 6.9. Theoretical force-extension curves compared with typical curve for rubber.

The uniform two-dimensional strain may be treated in exactly the same way. Fig. 6.10 shows the stress-strain relations for this type of strain, using the same two values of chain length.

These two sets of curves illustrate the general properties of the non-Gaussian network. In contrast to the corresponding Gaussian relations, the amount of extension has a finite limit. As this limit is approached the force rises more and more rapidly. In James and Guth's theory two parameters are required to define the properties of the non-Gaussian network, the first $G$ determines the vertical scale or modulus in the region of low strains, while the second $\kappa$ determines the maximum extensibility. In the author's theory these parameters are each related quantitatively to the chain length or molecular weight between junction points, which thus becomes the only independent parameter. The modulus $G$ is inversely proportional to the chain length, while the maximum extensibility is proportional to the square root of the chain length.

For comparison with experiment, typical stress-strain relations for a latex rubber vulcanized with 2 per cent. of sulphur

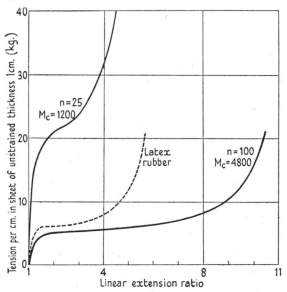

FIG. 6.10. Theoretical stress-strain curves for two-dimensional extension compared with typical curve for rubber.

and an accelerator are included in Figs. 6.9 and 6.10. This particular rubber was chosen rather than the 8 per cent. sulphur rubber studied in Chapter V, on account of its higher tensile strength. It will be seen that in the region of low strains the curves for this rubber are not far removed from the theoretical curves for $M_c = 4,800$. Actually, the best agreement was obtained with $M_c = 4,100$. But in maximum extensibility the experimental figures are distinctly less than the theoretical, the discrepancy being estimated at 40 per cent. for the two-dimensional strain and 20 per cent. for the simple elongation.

A discrepancy of this amount might be due to the neglect of the volume occupied by the atoms in the calculation of the statistical distribution of chain displacement lengths. If, instead of the theoretical 1·4 random links per isoprene unit we had chosen W. Kuhn and H. Kuhn's 'experimental' figure of 2·8 isoprene units per random link, the maximum extensibility to be expected would have been reduced by a factor of 2, which would bring the theoretical extensibility slightly below the experimental.

It should be pointed out, also, that the conditions to which the experimental data refer diverge in a number of respects from the ideal conditions implied by the theory. More particularly, the stress-strain curves at high strains are subject to rather large hysteresis effects, and therefore do not correspond to reversible conditions. Also the shape of the curves is certainly affected by crystallization, which becomes increasingly important with increasing strain. Flory (1946) and others have been inclined to attribute the existence of the upward curvature of the stress-strain curve to crystallization, but this is almost certainly incorrect, because, firstly, the shape is only slightly affected by raising the temperature to 100° C., where crystallization is very much reduced, and secondly, GR-S, which does not crystallize, shows a similar upward curvature at high extensions.† It seems more reasonable to conclude that the *general* shape of the stress-strain curves is to be interpreted on the basis of the non-Gaussian statistical theory, which, as we have seen, accounts in a more or less quantitative way for the absolute magnitudes of both the modulus and the extensibility. In matters of detail, however, neither the theory nor the experimental data can be regarded as sufficiently precise to justify a strict comparison.

† Treloar, unpublished work.

# CHAPTER VII

# DEVIATIONS FROM THE STATISTICAL THEORY

## 1. Introduction

IN assessing the merits of the statistical theory, it is important to bear in mind that the laws of elastic deformation to which it leads are an inevitable consequence of the fundamental assumptions upon which it is based. These assumptions, in their turn, were not introduced with the object of providing a means of deriving these particular results, but were based on considerations concerning the properties of molecules evolved from comparatively unrelated fields of inquiry. Moreover, the laws derived from the theoretical model had not previously been formulated on an empirical basis. If we limit ourselves to the region of small and moderate (as distinct from very large) deformations, we find that the properties of a well-vulcanized rubber can be satisfactorily represented by the theoretical relations at least to a first approximation, and also that the absolute value of the one molecular or physical parameter involved in these equations agrees in order of magnitude with the value experimentally found.

However, with a theory of such generality, in which specific details of structure are intentionally ignored for the sake of simplicity, it would not be expected that the theoretical formulae would apply in a quantitatively accurate manner to any actual material. It is therefore not surprising to find, in the case of a typical vulcanized rubber, deviations from the theoretical relations which may amount to as much as 25 per cent. of the calculated stresses, in the region of moderately large strains. The kind of deviations observed are well shown, for example, in Fig. 5.7, in which the data for the different types of strain diverge more and more from a single straight line through the origin as the strains increase in magnitude. Up to the present these divergences have been referred to only in passing, because the primary purpose was to concentrate our attention on the general agreement between the theoretical and experimental relations.  Having now established this general agreement, we may profitably turn back and reconsider the whole problem, paying particular attention to these relatively small, but possibly important, deviations from the ideal theoretical behaviour.

## 2. Experiments on general homogeneous strain

For such a general examination it is advantageous to extend the experimental study beyond the simple types of strain considered in Chapter V so as to include strains of the most general type.  In the most general type of homogeneous strain the three principal extension ratios $\lambda_1$, $\lambda_2$, and $\lambda_3$ may have any values, consistent, of course, with the incompressibility condition

$$\lambda_1 \lambda_2 \lambda_3 = 1. \tag{7.1}$$

This means that two of the three principal extension ratios may be considered as independent variables which may assume any chosen values; the third is then necessarily determined.  The general problem is to relate the three principal stresses $t_1$, $t_2$, and $t_3$ (Fig. 4.1) to the three principal extension ratios.  The statistical theory requires this relation to be of the form

$$t_1 - t_2 = G(\lambda_1^2 - \lambda_2^2), \tag{7.2}$$

where $G$ is a physical constant of the material.

To devise an experiment which will allow of the application of two independently variable strains in two perpendicular directions and the simultaneous measurement of the stresses is not altogether simple.  The technique employed by the author (Treloar, 1948) is not ideal, but seems to meet the requirements sufficiently well, and enables measurements of the stresses accompanying the general homogeneous strain to be carried out up to moderately large strains (e.g. $\lambda = 3$).  In this method a suitably marked sheet of rubber having the dimensions shown in Fig. 7.1 (a) is extended in two directions at right angles by means of strings attached to a number of projecting lugs on its perimeter.  Of the five strings attached to one side, the middle three were loaded with known weights while the two outermost were independently adjusted; in this way the effect of non-uniformity of strain in the neighbourhood of the edges could be largely overcome. This will be clear from Fig. 7.1 (b), from which it will be seen that the middle rectangle $ABCD$ is in a state of pure homogeneous strain. The two extension ratios in the plane of the sheet, $\lambda_1$ and $\lambda_2$, were directly measured, while the third extension ratio $\lambda_3$ in the direction of its thickness was calculated from the incompressibility relation (7.1). The principal stresses

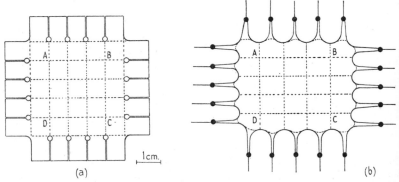

FIG. 7.1. Sheet of rubber in (a) unstrained and (b) strained state. The middle area $ABCD$ undergoes pure homogeneous strain.

$t_1$ and $t_2$ in the directions of $\lambda_1$ and $\lambda_2$ respectively were calculated from the weights applied to the sides $AB$ and $CD$ of the rectangular block $ABCD$. The third principal stress $t_3$ was of course zero.

The rubber used in these studies was a sheet of a 'pure gum' mix, vulcanized with 2 per cent. of sulphur in the presence of an accelerator. Experiments were made not only on the dry rubber but also on the same material when swollen in medicinal paraffin to about twice its normal volume. In Fig. 7.2 the difference of the two principal stresses in the plane of the sheet, $t_1-t_2$, is plotted against the difference of the squares of the corresponding extension ratios, $\lambda_1^2-\lambda_2^2$. For both the dry and swollen material the expected linear relation (7.2) is fairly closely satisfied, the agreement being rather more close in the case of the swollen rubber. In these experiments the values of the extension ratios $\lambda_1$ and $\lambda_2$ ranged from about 0·7 to 3·2 for the dry rubber, and from about 0·7 to 2·5 for the swollen material. From the slopes of the lines in Fig. 7.2 the values of

$G$ for the dry and swollen states were found to be 2·90 and 2·09 kg./cm.² respectively. Theoretically these values should be proportional to $v_r^{\frac{1}{3}}$ (eqn. 4.27), where $v_r$ is the volume fraction of rubber in the swollen state. With the value of $v_r$ used, namely 0·525, the ratio of the two values of $G$ in the dry and swollen rubber should therefore be 1·24, which is rather less

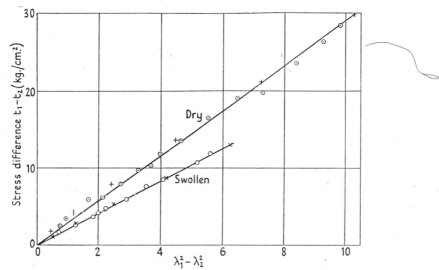

FIG. 7.2. Pure homogeneous strain. Difference of principal stresses v. $\lambda_1^2 - \lambda_2^2$. The crosses refer to simple elongation ($t_2 = 0$).

than the observed ratio of 1·39. The difference is presumably due to relaxation or breaking down of some of the 'cohesional' cross-linkages by the solvent. Apart from this difference, the data appear to fit the theoretical formula (7.2) rather well.

A different picture emerges if, instead of plotting the stress difference $t_1 - t_2$ against $\lambda_1^2 - \lambda_2^2$, we make use of the same data to plot $t_1$ and $t_2$ separately against $\lambda_1^2 - \lambda_3^2$ and $\lambda_2^2 - \lambda_3^2$ respectively. Since the stress $t_3$ is zero, we should have, from equations of the type (7.2)

$$\left.\begin{aligned} t_1 &= t_1 - t_3 = G(\lambda_1^2 - \lambda_3^2), \\ t_2 &= t_2 - t_3 = G(\lambda_2^2 - \lambda_3^2), \end{aligned}\right\} \tag{7.3}$$

and

so that a plot of $t_1$ or $t_2$ against $\lambda_1^2 - \lambda_3^2$ and $\lambda_2^2 - \lambda_3^2$ respectively should yield a straight line of slope $G$. Such a plot is shown in

Fig. 7.3 for the dry and in Fig. 7.4 for the swollen rubber. In these cases the theoretical relation breaks down, since the points fall not on a single straight line but on a series of discrete linear arrays. In any one of these linear arrays the force $f_1$ (corresponding to the stress $t_1$) is constant, while the other force $f_2$ is varied. (Since the area on which $f_1$ acts is a function of the

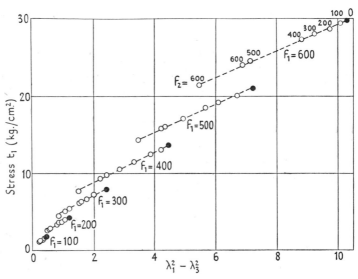

FIG. 7.3. Pure homogeneous strain, unswollen rubber. Stress $t_1$ v. $\lambda_1^2 - \lambda_3^2$. The black circles refer to simple elongation. $f_1$ and $f_2$ are forces in gm. acting on an unstrained area of $0\cdot0648$ cm.$^2$

strain, a constant force $f_1$ does not imply a constant stress $t_1$, but $f_1$ is proportional to $t_1/\lambda_1$.)

Not only does the linear relation between $t_1$ and $\lambda_1^2 - \lambda_3^2$ not apply, but $t_1$ is found to be not even a unique function of $\lambda_1^2 - \lambda_3^2$, since by suitable variations of $t_2$ it is possible to obtain two or more different values of $t_1$ for the same value of $\lambda_1^2 - \lambda_3^2$. This conclusion, if genuine, would therefore represent a rather serious departure from the behaviour to be expected from the statistical theory.

Before accepting this result at its face value, it seemed desirable to examine carefully the possibility that the effects observed might have been spurious, and due to some imper-

fection in the experimental technique. Three possible sources
of error were considered: (1) relaxation effects, (2) anisotropy
of the original sheet of rubber, and (3) non-uniformity of the
strain. Of these (1) was ruled out, firstly because the effects
were completely reproducible, and independent of the order of
application of the forces, and secondly because they were not

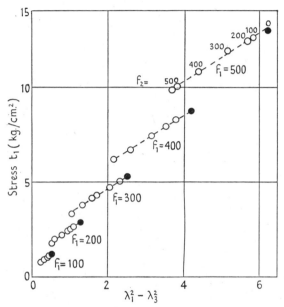

FIG. 7.4. Pure homogeneous strain, swollen rubber. Stress $t_1$ v. $\lambda_1^2 - \lambda_3^2$.
The black circles refer to simple elongation. $f_1$ and $f_2$ are forces in gm.
acting on an unstrained area of 0·0985 cm.²

very much affected by the swelling of the rubber, which from
the experiments of Gee and others (Chap. II) is known greatly
to accelerate the process of relaxation. Nor could crystallization
have played any part, since simultaneous measurement of the
optical double refraction showed that crystallization was not
present under the conditions of the experiment (cf. Chap.
VIII). The second possibility, that the sheet might have some
degree of anisotropy, due perhaps to the effect of rolling before
vulcanization, was rejected as a result of experiments on a latex
sheet, in which no such rolling or other comparable process

was involved. This material showed an entirely comparable behaviour. The third and most serious possibility, that there might have been some error introduced by the non-uniformity of the strain in the neighbourhood of the edges of the sheet, was tested indirectly by studying particular types of strain on the same sample of rubber by independent methods, in which such difficulties did not arise. Thus, the uniform two-dimensional strain ($\lambda_1 = \lambda_2$) was studied by the method of inflation (Chap. V), while the simple elongation was performed on a parallel-sided strip. In each case the results agreed to within 3 per cent. with those given by the original method; the points for simple elongation obtained in this way are indicated in Figs. 7.3 and 7.4.

The evidence therefore establishes beyond reasonable doubt that the pattern of points represented in Figs. 7.3 and 7.4 represents a genuine departure from the statistical theory.

Two questions now arise. Firstly, how can the fair agreement with the theory found when plotting $t_1 - t_2$ against $\lambda_1^2 - \lambda_2^2$ be reconciled with the marked disagreement shown when $t_1$ is plotted against $\lambda_1^2 - \lambda_3^2$? Secondly, is it possible to find some mathematical formula which will account satisfactorily for all the experimental observations?

## 3. Mooney's theory of large elastic deformations

The theory put forward by Mooney (1940) goes some way towards answering both these questions. This theory, which is of a rather general character, focuses attention on the *relations* between the stresses, for different types of strain. It is shown, on the basis of very simple assumptions, that if the stress-strain relation for one type of strain is given, that for another type of strain cannot be assumed to have any arbitrary form. Thus if the stress-strain relation for simple shear is given, the form of the stress-strain relations for other types of strain can be derived. The demonstration of these mutual relationships involves only considerations of logical or mathematical consistency; it is not dependent upon any particular physical or structural model.

Mooney considered two cases: (1) in which the stress-strain relation in simple shear is linear, and (2) in which the stress-strain relation in simple shear is an arbitrary (non-linear) function. In both cases the additional assumptions are introduced that the material is initially isotropic, and that it is incompressible. The simple case (1) leads to the following expression for the stored-energy function, or work of deformation per unit volume, in the general homogeneous strain, in terms of the three principal extension ratios $\lambda_1$, $\lambda_2$, and $\lambda_3$:

$$W_2 = C_1(\lambda_1^2+\lambda_2^2+\lambda_3^2-3)+C_2(1/\lambda_1^2+1/\lambda_2^2+1/\lambda_3^2-3). \quad (7.4)$$

This expression contains two independent parameters, $C_1$ and $C_2$, which are to be regarded as fundamental constants for any given material. The corresponding equation derived from the statistical theory, namely

$$W = \tfrac{1}{2}G(\lambda_1^2+\lambda_2^2+\lambda_3^2-3), \quad\quad\quad (7.5)$$

is seen to be a special case of Mooney's more general theory, in which one of these constants ($C_2$) vanishes. That the ideal rubber (from the standpoint of the statistical theory) should have properties consistent with Mooney's theory is, of course, to be expected, since it also satisfies Hooke's law in shear. The close connexion between the two theories was pointed out by Wall (1942), when he originally derived the linear shear relation from the statistical theory, and it was utilized by the author (Treloar, 1943 $d$) in the original formulation of the general equation (7.5).

When the stored-energy function is known, the stress-strain relations for any type of strain are determined. As an illustration, let us consider the case of a simple elongation, measured by an extension ratio $\alpha$. For this case Mooney's equation (7.4) reduces to

$$W_2 = C_1(\alpha^2+2/\alpha-3)+C_2(1/\alpha^2+2\alpha-3).$$

If $F$ is the applied tension, we have $F = dW_2/d\alpha$, and therefore

$$F = 2C_1(\alpha-1/\alpha^2)+2C_2(1-1/\alpha^3).$$

The general stress-strain relations, corresponding to a pure homogeneous strain, are derived by an essentially similar, though somewhat more complicated, process. Their form is represented by equation (7.11).

The more general form of Mooney's theory, in which the shear relation is non-linear, requires the introduction of additional terms, involving higher powers of $\lambda_1$, $\lambda_2$, and $\lambda_3$, into the stored-energy function. The next term in the series would be of the form

$$W_4 = A_4(\lambda_1^4 + \lambda_2^4 + \lambda_3^4 - 3) + B_4(1/\lambda_1^4 + 1/\lambda_2^4 + 1/\lambda_3^4 - 3), \quad (7.6)$$

while the corresponding general term is

$$W_{2n} = A_{2n}(\lambda_1^{2n} + \lambda_2^{2n} + \lambda_3^{2n} - 3) + B_{2n}(1/\lambda_1^{2n} + 1/\lambda_2^{2n} + 1/\lambda_3^{2n} - 3). \quad (7.7)$$

The total work, or stored-energy function in the general case, is therefore represented by the series

$$W = W_2 + W_4 + W_6 + \ldots + W_{2n}$$

involving $2n$ independent parameters.

## 4. Rivlin's contribution to the general theory

It is evident from this discussion of Mooney's theory that a fundamental significance is to be attached to the stored-energy function, for it is through this function that the interrelation of the different types of strain is brought about. It would therefore appear advantageous to take this function as a starting-point, rather than, as Mooney does, the form of the stress-strain relation in simple shear. This is, in fact, Rivlin's approach to the problem.†

It might seem that the arbitrary choice of a stored-energy function would give such wide scope that a theory based on this idea would not be sufficiently specific to be of real value. On reflection, however, it is found that the stored-energy function cannot be chosen completely arbitrarily, for, as pointed out by Rivlin, there are certain requirements of logical consistency which determine at least some of its properties. Firstly, if the material is considered to be isotropic in the unstrained state, the stored-energy function must clearly be symmetrical in $\lambda_1$, $\lambda_2$, and $\lambda_3$. Secondly, since the stored energy is unaltered

† Rivlin, private communication.

by a change of sign of two of the $\lambda$, corresponding to a rotation of the deformed body through $180°$, the stored energy must depend only on the *even* powers of the $\lambda$. It follows that the stored energy must be expressible in terms of the following three quantities, which, being independent of the choice of coordinate axes, may be called the *strain invariants*:

$$\left.\begin{aligned} I_1 &= \lambda_1^2 + \lambda_2^2 + \lambda_3^2 \\ I_2 &= \lambda_1^2\lambda_2^2 + \lambda_2^2\lambda_3^2 + \lambda_3^2\lambda_1^2 \\ I_3 &= \lambda_1^2\lambda_2^2\lambda_3^2. \end{aligned}\right\} \tag{7.8}$$

If we introduce the incompressibility condition we have, further,

$$I_3 = 1; \quad \text{and} \quad I_2 = 1/\lambda_1^2 + 1/\lambda_2^2 + 1/\lambda_3^2. \tag{7.8a}$$

The simplest stored-energy functions which can be chosen to represent the behaviour of an isotropic, incompressible, elastic material are therefore either

$$(1) \quad W_1 = C_1(I_1-3) = C_1(\lambda_1^2+\lambda_2^2+\lambda_3^2-3) \tag{7.9}$$

or $\quad (2) \quad W_2 = C_2(I_2-3) = C_2(1/\lambda_1^2+1/\lambda_2^2+1/\lambda_3^2-3).$ (7.10)

(The quantity $-3$ is introduced in order that $W$ shall vanish in the unstrained state.)

On examining the formulae (7.9) and (7.10) it is interesting to find that the former is the form derived from the statistical theory, while a combination of the two leads to Mooney's equation (7.4). More complex stored-energy functions would involve higher powers of $I_1$ and $I_2$, and therefore of the $\lambda$, and would introduce additional constants $C_3$, $C_4$, etc.

The value of Rivlin's approach turns largely on the question of whether the simpler forms of stored-energy function, such as, for example, (7.9) or (7.4), do in fact represent the properties of the real materials in which we are interested. This kind of situation is one which is frequently met in the process of scientific evolution. We aim first at a simple interpretation or law, and only when this fails do we proceed to a more complicated formulation. The specific contribution of Rivlin's theory is in pointing out where to look for simplicity, i.e. in the stored-energy function, rather than, say, the stress-strain relation in simple elongation. That the formula derived from the statistical theory should be one of the two most simple possible forms is indeed remarkable, and greatly strengthens the practical significance of Rivlin's theory. That the combination of the two most simple forms should produce Mooney's equation enhances still further the inherent interest of this point of view.

Some further aspects and developments of Rivlin's theoretical methods will be discussed at a later stage. We return here to the problem with which we set out, namely the interpretation of the experimental data for homogeneous strains. Let us examine the effect of the addition of a second term to the stored-energy function, as represented by Mooney's formula (7.4). To do this it is necessary to derive equations for the principal stresses in terms of the extension ratios. These are given by Mooney in a form which reduces to

$$t_1-t_2 = 2(C_1+C_2\lambda_3^2)(\lambda_1^2-\lambda_2^2). \tag{7.11}$$

Taking $t_1$ and $t_2$ as the principal stresses in the plane of the sheet, we have $t_3 = 0$, and therefore the individual stresses take the form
$$t_1 = t_1-t_3 = 2(C_1+C_2\lambda_2^2)(\lambda_1^2-\lambda_3^2). \tag{7.11 a}$$

Two equations of this type determine the stresses in terms of the principal extension ratios. In the experimental arrangement the forces (not the stresses) are the independent variables. If $F_1$ and $F_2$ are the forces, per unit area of the unstrained cross-section on which they act, then $t_1 = \lambda_1 F_1$ and $t_2 = \lambda_2 F_2$. The forces are then given by two equations corresponding to (7.11 a), i.e.
$$\left.\begin{aligned}\lambda_1 F_1 &= 2(C_1+C_2\lambda_2^2)(\lambda_1^2-\lambda_3^2) \\ \lambda_2 F_2 &= 2(C_1+C_2\lambda_1^2)(\lambda_2^2-\lambda_3^2),\end{aligned}\right\} \tag{7.12}$$

which, with the additional relation $\lambda_1\lambda_2\lambda_3 = 1$, have to be solved for the $\lambda$. The solution is easily obtained graphically, for particular values of $C_1$ and $C_2$. A particular solution, using the values $2C_1 = 1{\cdot}0$; $2C_2 = 0{\cdot}1$, is represented in Fig. 7.5 in a form comparable with the experimental plots of Figs. 7.3 and 7.4, i.e. by plotting $t_1$ against $\lambda_1^2-\lambda_3^2$. Comparing the theoretical solution with the experimental data for the swollen rubber (Fig. 7.4), the agreement is seen to be very close.

A more direct comparison may be made by plotting the experimental stress $t_1$ against $(1+C_2\lambda_2^2/C_1)(\lambda_1^2-\lambda_3^2)$, choosing $C_2/C_1$ to give the best fit to a straight line. Such a plot is shown in Fig. 7.6. For the swollen rubber a satisfactory line is obtained with a value of $0\cdot1$ for $C_2/C_1$. Its slope is $2C_1$, which is found to be $2\cdot00$ kg./cm.² Hence the swollen rubber may be completely

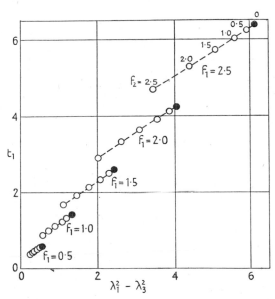

FIG. 7.5. Mooney's equation, with $2C_1 = 1\cdot0$, $2C_2 = 0\cdot1$.

described by Mooney's formula, using two constants having the values $C_1 = 1\cdot00$ kg./cm.², $C_2 = 0\cdot1$ kg./cm.² The data for the dry rubber, on the other hand, cannot be fitted to a straight line with any choice of the ratio $C_2/C_1$. They may, however, be brought on to a single curve, by putting $C_2/C_1 = 0\cdot05$. This means that Mooney's equation, though providing a better approximation than the statistical theory, does not completely represent the behaviour of this particular rubber in the dry state.

From these observations it is concluded that the rubber behaves more simply when swollen than when dry. It must also be inferred that in the dry state it does not obey Hooke's law in simple shear, though in the swollen state it does obey this law. Presumably the behaviour in the dry state could be accounted for by the inclusion of further terms, involving powers of $\lambda$ higher than the second, in the stored-energy function, but the limited value of an expression containing three or more

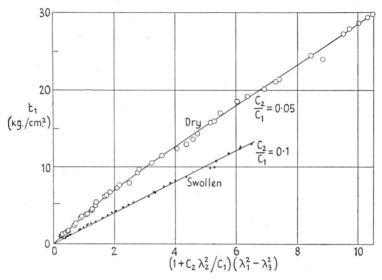

FIG. 7.6. Alternative representation of data in Figs. 7.3 and 7.4, on the basis of Mooney's equation.

adjustable parameters hardly justifies the further exploration of the problem along these lines.

To return to the swollen rubber data, the apparent agreement with the statistical theory in the case when $t_1 - t_2$ is plotted against $\lambda_1^2 - \lambda_2^2$ can now be understood. The extension ratio $\lambda_3$ being always less than unity, $\lambda_3^2$ is generally small compared with 1. Since also $C_2/C_1$ is small (i.e. 0·1) the term $C_2\lambda_3^2$ in (7.11) is never more than one-tenth of the term $C_1$, and is usually very much smaller. This means that except when the strains are quite small the stress-strain relation (7.11) will be indistinguishable from the corresponding statistical formula (7.2).

Some further interesting properties of Mooney's equation are illustrated in Fig. 7.7, which represents the dependence of $t_1 - t_3$

on $\lambda_1^2-\lambda_3^2$ for the three simplest types of strain, elongation, compression, and shear. The shear relation is linear and has the slope $2(C_1+C_2)$. The curve for simple elongation is not linear, though it approximates to a linear form at moderately large elongations, with, however, a lower slope $(2C_1)$ than the

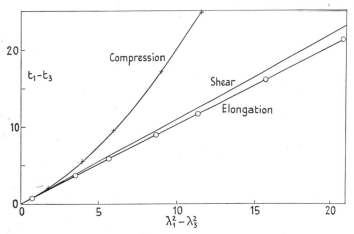

FIG. 7.7. Theoretical curves for different types of strain, using Mooney's formula, with $2C_1 = 1\cdot0$, $2C_2 = 0\cdot1$. (Cf. Fig. 5.7.)

shear line. The compression curve becomes increasingly divergent from the shear line as the strain is increased. All three curves converge to a single line at small strains.

These features of the theoretical stress-strain relations are closely paralleled by the experimental curves illustrated in Fig. 5.7 for the corresponding types of strain. It is evident that for this compound also Mooney's equation gives a better representation of the actual behaviour than the formulae derived from the statistical theory.

More recently Rivlin (1947) has carried out an experimental study of the torsion of a rubber cylinder. This work, which is discussed in Chapter XIII, led quite independently to the conclusion that the Mooney formula gives a more accurate representation of the behaviour of vulcanized rubber than the statistical theory. The value obtained for $C_2/C_1$ in these experiments was about $0\cdot14$.

## 5. Discussion of results

The general conclusion to be drawn from the experiments on homogeneous strain, together with a number of other independent results referred to in this chapter, is that the formulae derived from the statistical theory, involving, as they do, only a single adjustable parameter, can be regarded as representing the behaviour of real rubbers only to a first approximation, and appear to become increasingly inadequate as the amount of strain is increased. A better approximation to the actual behaviour is obtained by including additional terms in the stored-energy function. The addition of one such term leads to a second approximation, Mooney's equation, involving two independent parameters, which accounts quantitatively for the behaviour of the particular rubber examined in the swollen state, and gives a much closer fit to the data for the dry rubber. The accurate representation of the properties of the dry rubber would appear to require the inclusion of still more terms in the stored-energy function, but this has not been followed up.

It must be emphasized that the inclusion of higher terms in the stored-energy function is an entirely arbitrary procedure, which tells us nothing of the physical or molecular mechanism involved. The point of interest, which is brought out by Rivlin, and implied by Mooney, is that, when a choice of stored-energy function is made, the stress-strain relations for any homogeneous strain are automatically determined. The process of modifying or correcting the stored-energy function to suit a set of data is thus nothing more than the three-dimensional analogue of simple curve-fitting. Up to the present no molecular hypothesis which might explain the type of deviations from the statistical formulae which have been observed has been found.

# CHAPTER VIII

# THE PHOTO-ELASTIC PROPERTIES OF RUBBER

## 1. Isotropic and anisotropic materials

IT is well known that many crystals possess the property of splitting a ray of light incident on their surface into two distinct refracted rays. This phenomenon, which is known as double refraction, arises from the fact that such crystals have different physical and optical properties in different directions. It is only the most highly symmetrical types of crystal structure, such as the cubic class (of which rock-salt is a familiar example), which are physically and optically isotropic (i.e. the same in all directions) and therefore do not show double refraction.

Unlike crystalline materials, substances such as glass or rubber, whose atomic structure is more or less irregular, are normally isotropic in physical properties, as would be expected. But if such materials are deformed, their structural uniformity is disturbed; they cease to be isotropic, and begin to exhibit properties in some ways akin to those of an unsymmetrical crystal. In particular they show double refraction or birefringence, which is a rather sensitive indicator of the structural dissymmetry introduced by the strain.

This property of birefringence due to straining, discovered by Brewster in 1816, is one which has already been investigated in considerable detail in the case of hard materials such as glasses and plastics. It is a property which has been put to practical use in a variety of ways, among which may be mentioned, for example, the study of residual stresses in manufactured articles of glass, and the determination of the stress-distribution in engineering structures from the optical study of plastic models. Such applications have been rendered possible through the development of the science of photo-elasticity, which deals with the relation between the birefringence and the stresses or strains, and the experimental technique by which the optical measurements are carried out.

The study of the photo-elastic properties of rubber-like

materials is of comparatively recent development, and it is only within the last few years that a quantitative understanding of the phenomena encountered in this field has been achieved. The subject is complicated by the fact that double refraction in rubber may arise from two distinct causes. There is, first, a part which is related directly to the strain, the genuine 'strain-birefringence', and in addition, there is a contribution due to crystallization (when the deformation is such that crystallization takes place), arising from the fact that the crystallites are themselves doubly refracting. In the present chapter we shall be concerned mainly with the true strain-birefringence.

## 2. Double refraction and its measurement

In an isotropic medium the refractive index is a constant, independent of direction. In an anisotropic medium, on the

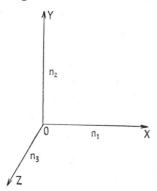

FIG. 8.1. Principal refractive indices in an anisotropic medium.

other hand, the refractive index depends on the direction in which the light is propagated, or more accurately, on the direction of the electric vector in the transverse electromagnetic wave. The optical properties of the medium are completely determined if we specify the three principal refractive indices $n_1$, $n_2$, and $n_3$ corresponding to a particular set of three mutually perpendicular directions $OX$, $OY$, $OZ$ of the electric vector (Fig. 8.1) which form the principal axes of the so-called 'refractive index ellipsoid'. Consider a ray of light travelling in the direction $OX$. The refractive index may be either $n_2$ or $n_3$ according to whether the direction of the electric vector is parallel to $OY$ or $OZ$. For other directions of electric vector, the ray may be resolved into two components having the refractive indices $n_2$ and $n_3$, i.e. there will be double refraction. The same considerations apply with respect to propagation along $OY$ or $OZ$.

From the optical point of view crystals fall into three classes.

If the three principal refractive indices $n_1$, $n_2$, and $n_3$ are equal, the crystal is isotropic, i.e. does not show double refraction. If two of the indices are equal, and the third different, it shows double refraction for all ray directions except one, which is called the optic axis. Crystals of this class are called uniaxial. If all three indices are different, there is double refraction in

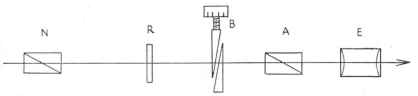

FIG. 8.2. Experimental arrangement for measurement of double refraction. *N*, polarizing Nicol prism. *R*, specimen. *B*, Babinet compensator. *A*, analysing Nicol prism. *E*, eyepiece.

all directions except two. Crystals of this class, which is the most unsymmetrical, are called biaxial. If rubber is stretched (or compressed) in one direction it becomes optically uniaxial, while if stretched unequally in two directions it becomes optically biaxial.

The measurement of double refraction therefore involves the determination of the difference between two principal refractive indices, for light polarized in two mutually perpendicular planes. Since in the case of strain-birefringence this difference is usually small, a sensitive method has to be adopted for its measurement. The usual method makes use of interference effects between the two rays travelling with different velocities through the material. The experimental arrangement, illustrated diagrammatically in Fig. 8.2, consists essentially of a polarizing Nicol prism *N* set so that the plane of polarization of the light incident on the specimen *R* makes an angle of 45° with the direction of the principal extensions, a Babinet compensator *B*, by which the double refraction is actually measured, and an analysing Nicol *A*, set at right angles to the polarizer.

To understand the action of the compensator it is necessary to consider briefly the phenomena of interference in doubly refracting materials. Let *OP* (Fig. 8.3) represent the plane of the electric vector in the incident wave, and let $OA$ and $OB$ be the directions of the principal extensions in the rubber, corresponding to the principal refractive indices $n_1$ and $n_2$ respectively. The incident wave of amplitude $OP$ may be resolved into two component waves of amplitude $Oa$ and $Ob$, polarized respectively in the planes $OA$ and $OB$, and travelling

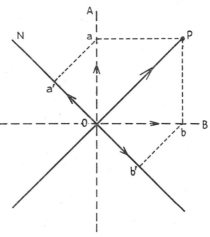

FIG. 8.3. Interference effects. $OP$, plane of polarizer.
$OA$, $OB$, principal axes of strain. $ON$, plane of analyser.

with velocities $c/n_1$ and $c/n_2$, where $c$ is the velocity of light *in vacuo*. Being polarized in planes at right angles to one another, these two rays will not produce destructive interference. This may be brought about, however, by inserting in the light beam an analysing Nicol $N$, crossed with the polarizer. The analyser will transmit components $Oa'$ and $Ob'$ of equal amplitude and polarized in the same plane. If the material is isotropic these components, being in opposite phase, will interfere to produce zero intensity of illumination. If, however, the material is not isotropic, there will be an *optical path difference* $\Delta$ between the two rays, which will in general lead to the transmission of light. For monochromatic light of (vacuum) wave-length $\lambda_0$ the intensity will be a maximum when

$$\Delta = (p + \tfrac{1}{2})\lambda_0 \qquad (8.1\,a)$$

and zero when    $\Delta = p\lambda_0 \quad (p = 0, 1, 2, ...).$ $\qquad (8.1\,b)$

The path difference $\Delta$ is proportional to the thickness $d$ of the specimen. Since the number of wave-lengths in the distance $d$ is $d/\lambda$ and since also $\lambda_1 = \lambda_0/n_1$ and $\lambda_2 = \lambda_0/n_2$, the relation between path difference and birefringence $n_1 - n_2$ is

$$\Delta = (n_1 - n_2)\frac{d}{\lambda_0}, \qquad (8.2)$$

$\lambda_1$ and $\lambda_2$ being the wave-lengths corresponding to the refractive indices $n_1$ and $n_2$.

According to (8.1) and (8.2) the intensity of transmitted light will pass through a succession of alternate maxima and minima as either $d$ or $n_1 - n_2$ is continuously increased. A wedge of doubly-refracting material (e.g. quartz) will therefore be crossed by a series of parallel fringes when viewed between crossed Nicols in monochromatic light, each successive fringe (measured from the tip) representing an increase of one wave-length in the optical path difference between the two rays.

The Babinet compensator makes use of two quartz wedges of equal angle and opposite birefringences. At the point where the thicknesses are equal there appears a dark band, corresponding to zero resultant path difference, while on either side there are parallel bands, corresponding to $+1$, $+2$,... and $-1$, $-2$,... wave-lengths. By means of a micrometer screw one wedge may be displaced through a known distance, in such a way that any particular fringe may be brought into coincidence with the central cross-wire. The compensator is therefore a device for introducing a measurable optical path difference.

In practice, it is convenient to work with white light, in which case there is a central dark band with coloured bands on either side. The compensator is adjusted so that the central band coincides with the cross-wire. On introducing the specimen whose birefringence is to be measured, the dark band is shifted to a new position. The quartz wedge is then displaced until the original position of the dark band is restored. The path difference in the specimen under these conditions is equal and opposite to the path difference introduced by the compensator.

## 3. The optical properties of a molecular network

The refractive index of a material is a function of its response to the electric field of the light wave, or more specifically, to its polarizability. By polarization we mean the separation of positive and negative charges to form a dipole; it is measured by the dipole moment per unit volume. The polarizability is the polarization produced by unit field-strength. The greater the polarizability, the higher is the refractive index, the relation between refractive index $n$ and polarizability $P$ being of the form

$$\frac{n^2-1}{n^2+2} = \frac{4\pi}{3} P. \tag{8.3}$$

If the medium is optically anisotropic, it follows that the polarizability is different in different directions. In the most general case we have three principal polarizabilities corresponding to the directions of the three principal refractive indices, each of which is governed by a relation of the type (8.3).

### Kuhn and Grün's theory of birefringence

The theoretical treatment of strain-birefringence in rubber has been worked out by W. Kuhn and Grün (1942), on the general basis of the statistical theory discussed in Chapters IV and VI. They consider first the optical properties of a single long-chain molecule, which for theoretical purposes is assumed, as before, to be representable by a chain of equal, randomly jointed links. The only additional feature which needs to be introduced is concerned with the optical properties of the chain. These are represented, in W. Kuhn and Grün's theory, by two polarizabilities $\alpha_1$ and $\alpha_2$ respectively parallel and perpendicular to the direction of the link.

The first problem is the calculation of the principal polarizabilities of a single long-chain molecule. The chain is held with its ends separated by a vector distance $r$, which may be taken for convenience along the axis $OX$ of a rectangular coordinate system $X$, $Y$, $Z$, and the polarizability is calculated for two directions of electric field, (1) along the axis $OX$, and (2) at right angles to $OX$. To solve this problem it is necessary first to derive the distribution of link angles $\theta$ with respect to the direction $OX$. The complete distribution function derived by Kuhn and Grün, which has been referred to earlier (eqn. 6.1), may be written

$$dn_{\theta,\phi} = \frac{n\beta}{\sinh\beta} e^{\beta\cos\theta} \tfrac{1}{2} \sin\theta \, d\theta \frac{d\phi}{2\pi}, \qquad (8.4)$$

where $dn_{\theta,\phi}$ is the number of links in the range of angular coordinates represented by $d\theta$, $d\phi$ and $n$ is the total number of links. The quantity $\beta$ in this equation is the inverse Langevin function $\mathscr{L}^{-1}(r/nl)$.

Knowing the number of links at angles $\theta$, $\phi$ it is then only necessary to find the components of polarizability parallel and perpendicular to $OX$ for the individual link, and to integrate over the whole number of links. Denoting the component polarizabilities by $\alpha_\parallel$ and $\alpha_\perp$ respectively, we have, from standard optical theory

$$\left. \begin{aligned} \alpha_\parallel &= \alpha_1\cos^2\theta + \alpha_2\sin^2\theta \\ \alpha_\perp &= (\alpha_1-\alpha_2)\sin^2\theta\cos^2\phi + \alpha_2 \end{aligned} \right\} \qquad (8.5)$$

and the corresponding total chain polarizabilities are therefore

$$\left. \begin{aligned} \gamma_1 &= \int \alpha_\parallel \, dn, \\ \gamma_2 &= \int \alpha_\perp \, dn. \end{aligned} \right\} \qquad (8.6)$$

Evaluation of these integrals, with the help of (8.4) and (8.5) gives, for the polarizability $\gamma_1$ parallel to $OX$, i.e. parallel to the vector $r$ joining the ends of the chain,

$$\gamma_1 = n\left[\alpha_1 - (\alpha_1-\alpha_2)\frac{2r/nl}{\mathscr{L}^{-1}(r/nl)}\right], \qquad (8.7\,a)$$

while the polarizability $\gamma_2$ in directions at right angles to the vector $r$ is

$$\gamma_2 = n\left[\alpha_2 + (\alpha_1-\alpha_2)\frac{r/nl}{\mathscr{L}^{-1}(r/nl)}\right]. \qquad (8.7\,b)$$

The difference of these two polarizabilities, which represents the optical anisotropy of the molecule, is therefore

$$\gamma_1 - \gamma_2 = n(\alpha_1-\alpha_2)\left[1 - \frac{3r/nl}{\mathscr{L}^{-1}(r/nl)}\right] \qquad (8.8\,a)$$

$$= n(\alpha_1-\alpha_2)\left[\frac{3}{5}\left(\frac{r}{nl}\right)^2 + \frac{36}{175}\left(\frac{r}{nl}\right)^4 + \frac{108}{875}\left(\frac{r}{nl}\right)^6 + \cdots\right]. \qquad (8.8\,b)$$

The function (8.8 $a$) is shown in Fig. 8.4, in which the ordinates are $(\gamma_1-\gamma_2)/n(\alpha_1-\alpha_2)$, the anisotropy relative to that for the fully extended chain, which is of course, $n(\alpha_1-\alpha_2)$. The series expansion (8.8 $b$) shows that for small extensions the anisotropy is proportional to the square of the distance $r$ between the chain ends. This formula also leads to an interesting result for the

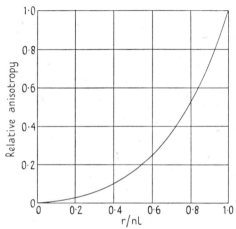

Fig. 8.4. Optical anisotropy as function of relative
length of random chain.

anisotropy of a chain in the free or unrestrained state. For such a chain the average or mean square length is given by $\overline{r^2} = nl^2$. Insertion in (8.8 $b$) gives, for the anisotropy of such a chain,

$$\gamma_1-\gamma_2 = \tfrac{3}{5}(\alpha_1-\alpha_2), \qquad (8.8\,c)$$

i.e. the mean optical anisotropy of a randomly kinked chain in the absence of external restraints is three-fifths of the aniso-tropy of a single link of the chain.

In the application of the result represented by equations (8.7 $a$) and (8.7 $b$) to the network problem, Kuhn and Grün proceed by the following stages.

1. It is assumed that the network contains $N$ chains per unit volume. The vector distances $r$ between the ends of the chains (i.e. between junction points of the network) in the unstrained state are assumed to be all equal, and distributed randomly in direction.

2. On deformation, the assumption of an affine deformation of chain displacement length is introduced. This defines the length $r'$ and directional coordinates $\theta'$ and $\phi'$ (relative to the principal axes of strain) in terms of the initial length $r$ and angles $(\theta, \phi)$ and the ratio of stretch $\lambda$. (Cf. Fig. 4.2.)

3. The principal polarizabilities for a chain of length $r'$ are known (eqns. 8.7), and hence, with the help of equations (8.5) it is possible to write down the components of polarizability along the principal axes of strain for this particular chain.

4. The total components of polarizability parallel to the strain axes are then obtained by integration over all values of $\theta'$ and $\phi'$.

To obtain a result in a reasonably simple form, it is necessary to include only the first term in the series expansion for the molecular polarizabilities. With this approximation, the components of polarizability $P_\parallel$ and $P_\perp$ respectively parallel and perpendicular to the direction of extension, for the whole network, become

$$P_\parallel = N\left[\frac{n}{3}(\alpha_1+2\alpha_2)+\frac{2}{15}(\alpha_1-\alpha_2)\frac{\overline{r^2}}{nl^2}\left(\lambda^2-\frac{1}{\lambda}\right)\right], \qquad (8.9\,a)$$

$$P_\perp = N\left[\frac{n}{3}(\alpha_1+2\alpha_2)-\frac{1}{15}(\alpha_1-\alpha_2)\frac{\overline{r^2}}{nl^2}\left(\lambda^2-\frac{1}{\lambda}\right)\right]. \qquad (8.9\,b)$$

The only remaining step is to transform these polarizabilities into the corresponding principal refractive indices $n_1$ and $n_2$ parallel and perpendicular to the direction of extension. For this purpose use is made of the relation between refractivity and polarizability, represented by (8.3). This formula is applied to each of the expressions (8.9 a) and (8.9 b). The quantity in which we are interested is the birefringence, or difference of principal refractive indices $n_1-n_2$. If this is small (as it invariably is) it is convenient to introduce the algebraical approximation

$$\frac{n_1^2-1}{n_1^2+2}-\frac{n_2^2-1}{n_2^2+2} \simeq \frac{6\bar{n}}{(\bar{n}^2+2)^2}(n_1-n_2), \qquad (8.10)$$

where $\bar{n}$ is the mean refractive index. If, in addition we put

$\overline{r^2} = nl^2$ in (8.9 a) and (8.9 b), the expression for the birefringence then becomes

$$n_1 - n_2 = \frac{2\pi}{45} \frac{(\bar{n}^2 + 2)^2}{\bar{n}} N(\alpha_1 - \alpha_2)\left(\lambda^2 - \frac{1}{\lambda}\right). \qquad (8.11)$$

The birefringence is thus not a linear function of the extension (except for very small extensions) but is proportional to $(\lambda^2 - 1/\lambda)$. It is also proportional to $(\alpha_1 - \alpha_2)$, the anisotropy of the individual link of the statistical chain, and to $N$, the number of chains per unit volume of the network.

There is a very close relation between the birefringence and the stress. For by equation (4.16) the stress (referred to the actual section) is

$$t = NkT(\lambda^2 - 1/\lambda), \qquad (8.12)$$

and therefore

$$n_1 - n_2 = \frac{2\pi}{45kT} \frac{(\bar{n}^2 + 2)^2}{\bar{n}} (\alpha_1 - \alpha_2)t, \qquad (8.13)$$

or

$$n_1 - n_2 = Ct, \qquad (8.13\,a)$$

where $C$ is a constant. This equation shows that the birefringence (at a given temperature) should be proportional to the stress. This result is equivalent to Brewster's law, referred to above. The constant $C$ is called the *stress-optical coefficient*.

### The general homogeneous strain

Kuhn and Grün's analysis was limited to the case of simple elongation. Under this type of strain rubber behaves as a uni-axial crystal; a crystal, that is, which possesses cylindrical symmetry with respect to a single direction, the optic axis, and which is characterized by two refractive indices for light having directions of electric vector respectively parallel and perpendicular to the optic axis.

In the general homogeneous strain, it may be assumed that the principal axes of the refractive index ellipsoid will coincide with the principal axes of strain. The problem then is to calculate the principal refractive indices in these three directions, as functions of the principal extension ratios $\lambda_1$, $\lambda_2$, and $\lambda_3$.

In the treatment of this problem the author (Treloar, 1947 a) found the direct method of approach used by Kuhn and Grün to be too complicated mathematically to be useful. The method of solution actually adopted depended upon the following artifice. The assembly of $r$-vectors representing the $N$ chains in the network was divided up into $N/3$ sets of three mutually perpendicular chains. Such a division may obviously be carried out, without interfering with the randomness of the original distribution. One set of three chains was then subjected to an 'affine deformation', corresponding to three principal stretches parallel to the axes of an $XYZ$ coordinate system. The directions of the three $r$-vectors were related to the directions $OX$, $OY$, $OZ$ by a set of direction cosines $l$, $m$, $n$, etc. The contribution to the total polarizability in the directions of $OX$, $OY$, and $OZ$ due to this set of three chains was then calculated, using, as was done by Kuhn and Grün, only the first term in the expansion of equations (8.7 $a$) and (8.7 $b$). The result obtained, for the polarizability along $OX$, corresponding to the strain axis $\lambda_1$, was

$$\beta_x = n(\alpha_1 + 2\alpha_2) + (\alpha_1 - \alpha_2)\frac{r^2}{5nl^2}(2\lambda_1^2 - \lambda_2^2 - \lambda_3^2), \qquad (8.14)$$

with similar expressions for the polarizabilities in the other two directions. The interesting feature of equation (8.14) is that it does not contain the direction cosines $l$, $m$, $n$, etc., so that *the components of polarizability, for a set of three mutually perpendicular chains, are independent of the directions of the chains with respect to the axes of strain.*

This result leads immediately to the required solution for the whole assembly. For, having solved the problem for one set of chains, we have solved it for all. It is only necessary to multiply the component polarizability by $N/3$, the number of sets in the assembly. Putting $\overline{r^2} = nl^2$, the components of polarizability for the whole network thus become

$$\left.\begin{aligned}
P_x &= N[(n/3)(\alpha_1 + 2\alpha_2) + \tfrac{1}{15}(\alpha_1 - \alpha_2)(2\lambda_1^2 - \lambda_2^2 - \lambda_3^2)] \\
P_y &= N[(n/3)(\alpha_1 + 2\alpha_2) + \tfrac{1}{15}(\alpha_1 - \alpha_2)(2\lambda_2^2 - \lambda_3^2 - \lambda_1^2)] \\
P_z &= N[(n/3)(\alpha_1 + 2\alpha_2) + \tfrac{1}{15}(\alpha_1 - \alpha_2)(2\lambda_3^2 - \lambda_1^2 - \lambda_2^2)].
\end{aligned}\right\} \quad (8.15)$$

From these three principal polarizabilities the corresponding refractivities are obtained with the help of equation (8.3), i.e.

$$\frac{n_1^2-1}{n_1^2+2} = \frac{4\pi N}{3}\left[\frac{n}{3}(\alpha_1+2\alpha_2)+\tfrac{1}{15}(\alpha_1-\alpha_2)(2\lambda_1^2-\lambda_2^2-\lambda_3^2)\right] \quad (8.16)$$

with similar expressions for $n_2$ and $n_3$.

We are concerned not with the absolute values of refractive indices, but with their differences. The difference of any two is seen from equation (8.16) to be of the form

$$n_1-n_2 = \frac{(\bar{n}^2+2)^2}{\bar{n}}\frac{2\pi N}{45}(\alpha_1-\alpha_2)(\lambda_1^2-\lambda_2^2). \quad (8.17)$$

This difference $n_1-n_2$ gives a measure of the birefringence for a ray of light propagated along the direction of $\lambda_3$. The result may be expressed as a general law, as follows: *The difference of any two principal refractive indices is proportional to the difference of the squares of the corresponding extension ratios.*

As in simple elongation, so in the general strain, there exists a close parallelism between the birefringence and the stress. For by equation (4.11) the difference of the principal stresses $t_1$ and $t_2$ is

$$t_1-t_2 = NkT(\lambda_1^2-\lambda_2^2), \quad (8.18)$$

and therefore

$$n_1-n_2 = \frac{(\bar{n}^2+2)^2}{\bar{n}}\frac{2\pi}{45kT}(\alpha_1-\alpha_2)(t_1-t_2), \quad (8.19)$$

or

$$n_1-n_2 = C(t_1-t_2), \quad (8.19\,a)$$

which means that *the difference of refractive indices for light propagated along one of the principal axes of strain is proportional to the difference of the corresponding principal stresses.*

The two results given in italics are the fundamental laws of photo-elasticity for a rubber-like material. The second is the generalized form of Brewster's law, which is thus shown to be applicable to a large deformation of a rubber, as well as to a small deformation of a hard elastic solid, though for a quite different reason. The first law has no analogue in classical photo-elastic theory, but reduces to the classical formula (birefringence proportional to strain-difference) when the deformations are small. The formulae (8.17) and (8.19) reduce to the simpler forms (8.11) and (8.13) for the case of a simple elongation.

Two further points should be mentioned. Firstly, it may be shown (Treloar, 1947 a) that the assumption that all the chains have the same initial $r$-vectors is not essential. The same results may be obtained for any distribution of $r$-vectors, provided that the chain contour lengths are all equal, and that the mean square displacement length is given by $\overline{r^2} = nl^2$.

Secondly, it is clear that the use of the first term only in the series expansion for the inverse Langevin function implies that the strains are not too large. This restriction is formally equivalent to the 'Gaussian' limitation previously encountered in the network elasticity theory. The optical relations deduced above therefore apply only to the 'Gaussian' network.

## The effect of swelling

It is a simple matter to extend the theory to the case of a rubber swollen by a solvent. For this purpose it is assumed that the solvent is optically neutral, and isotropic, even when the rubber is strained. The solvent is therefore assumed to affect the optical properties only indirectly, by altering the mean value of chain extensions. In the unstrained state the mean chain extension $\sqrt{(\overline{r^2})}$ is assumed to be proportional to the linear dimensions of the swollen rubber, i.e. to $1/v_r^{\frac{1}{3}}$, where $v_r$ is the volume fraction of rubber in the mixture. For a network of $N$ chains occupying unit volume in the unswollen state, the effect on the polarizabilities is then simply to alter $\overline{r^2}$ in equation (8.14) from $nl^2$ to $nl^2/v_r^{\frac{2}{3}}$. A further factor of $v_r$ has to be introduced to relate the polarizabilities to unit volume in the swollen state. In this way the birefringence relation (8.17) becomes modified to

$$n_1 - n_2 = \frac{(\bar{n}^2 + 2)^2}{\bar{n}} \frac{2\pi N}{45} (\alpha_1 - \alpha_2) v_r^{\frac{1}{3}} (\lambda_1^2 - \lambda_2^2). \qquad (8.20)$$

This result means that, for a given state of strain (referred to the swollen state), the effect of swelling is to reduce the birefringence by the factor $v_r^{\frac{1}{3}}$. In other words, the birefringence is inversely proportional to the linear dimensions of the unstrained, swollen rubber.

It must be noted, however, that although the swelling liquid makes no direct contribution to the birefringence, its effect on $\bar{n}$, the mean refractive index, has to be taken into account if its refractive index differs from that of the rubber.

The effect of swelling on the stresses has been given in Chapter IV (p. 74). As with the birefringence, the only change is the inclusion of a factor $v_r^{\frac{1}{3}}$ on the right-hand side of equation (8.18). Hence the ratio of birefringence to stress is still given by equation (8.19). This ratio is therefore independent of the degree of swelling (except for a correction due to change in mean refractive index).

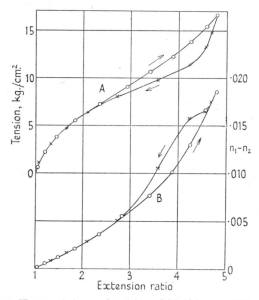

FIG. 8.5. Hysteresis in tension ($A$) and birefringence ($B$) curves.

## 4. Experimental investigations

Experimental work on birefringence in rubber may be directed towards two main objectives: (1) the examination of the applicability of the theoretical laws discussed in the last section, and (2) the study of crystallization phenomena. In this section we shall be concerned specifically with the first of these objectives, though some consideration of crystallization will be involved incidentally. A fuller examination of crystallization, by optical and other methods, will be made in the chapter following.

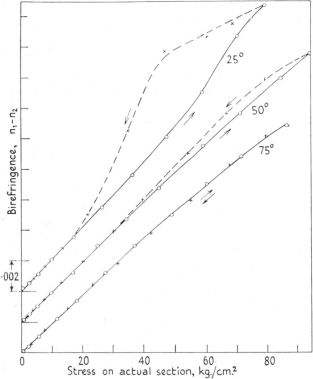

FIG. 8.6. Relation between birefringence and stress for natural rubber, at 25°, 50°, and 75° C. Circles, strain increasing. Crosses, strain decreasing.

Studies along these lines have recently been carried out by the author (Treloar, 1947 b). The typical behaviour of a rubber in simple elongation is represented in Fig. 8.5, which refers to a natural rubber vulcanized with 2 per cent. of sulphur and an accelerator. Both the tension curve (top) and the birefringence curve (bottom) show marked hysteresis in the same region of extension, but whereas the tension is lower on retraction than on extension, the birefringence is higher. Thus, when the birefringence is plotted against the stress (referred in this case to the strained cross-sectional area), the loop is still more pronounced (Fig. 8.6). However, at the lower stresses (up to an extension ratio of about 3·0), the extension and retraction points fall on a single straight line, in agreement with equation (8.13).

It is inferred that these hysteresis loops are the result of crystallization. This is confirmed by experiments at higher

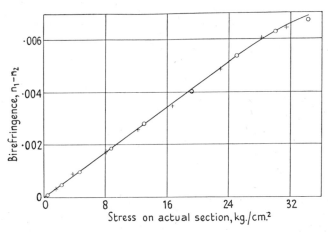

Fɪɢ. 8.7. Relation between birefringence and stress for GR-S rubber at 25° C. Circles, strain increasing. Crosses, strain decreasing.

temperatures (Fig. 8.6), which show a progressive diminution in the effects with rising temperature. At 75° C. the stress-birefringence relation was approximately linear up to an extension ratio of about 5. Curves taken with still higher extensions and at a temperature of 100° C. (not shown) showed a more noticeable curvature; this effect is due primarily to the upward curvature of the stress-strain curve at high extensions (the 'non-Gaussian' effect) which is not taken into consideration in the theory as described.

It is interesting to compare these results with the corresponding curves for a rubber which does not crystallize. Fig. 8.7 shows the tension and birefringence curve for such a rubber, a GR-S compound, vulcanized with 2 per cent. of sulphur and an accelerator. These data are taken from the author's un-published work. The hysteresis loops are noticeably absent, and although there is evidence of rather more relaxation, the stress-birefringence relation conforms well with the theory.

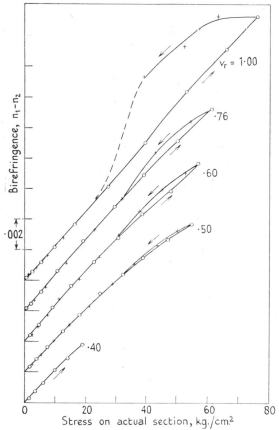

FIG. 8.8. Effect of swelling on hysteresis. $v_r$ = volume fraction of rubber in mixture.

Fig. 8.8 shows the effect of swelling in toluene on the stress-birefringence relation for the natural rubber compound. Swelling is seen to affect the hysteresis loops in a similar manner to increase of temperature. According to the theory the slope of the curve should be independent of the degree of swelling. This is seen to be approximately true.

The general homogeneous strain was also studied by the author (Treloar, 1948), who used for this purpose a sheet of the same rubber extended unequally in two directions by the method described in Chapter VII. The birefringence and the principal stresses were measured simultaneously.

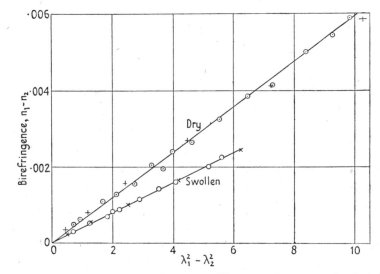

FIG. 8.9. Birefringence plotted against difference of squares of principal extension ratios, for dry and swollen rubber. (The crosses refer to simple elongation.)

Fig. 8.9 shows the variation of birefringence with the difference of the squares of the principal extension ratios $\lambda_1^2 - \lambda_2^2$ for the dry rubber, and for the same rubber swollen in medicinal paraffin to about twice its original volume. The expected linear relation (eqn. 8.20) seems to be closely approached. The slopes of the experimental lines are respectively 5·96 and 4·00 × 10⁻⁴, giving a ratio of 1·49, which compares with the theoretical ratio $(v_r^{-\frac{1}{3}})$ of 1·24. This discrepancy is probably due to relaxation, which, as was seen in Chapter II, is greatly facilitated by swelling, and which leads to a reduction in the effective number of network junction points.

The relation between birefringence and stress, for the same rubber, both dry and swollen, is depicted in Fig. 8.10. The points fall closely on a straight line, whose slope is only slightly affected by swelling. The agreement seems to be particularly good in the case of the swollen material, which again points to

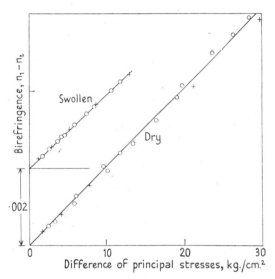

FIG. 8.10. Birefringence plotted against difference of principal stresses, for dry and swollen rubber. (The crosses refer to simple elongation.)

the conclusion that a swollen rubber corresponds rather more closely with the ideal theoretical network than the unswollen material.

## 5. The anisotropy of the rubber molecule

The theoretical relations (8.19) and (8.19 a) show that the stress-optical coefficient $C$ should be independent of $N$, the number of chains per unit volume of the network, and therefore of the degree of cross-linkage or vulcanization. In fact, $C$ should be a characteristic of the molecule of the rubber, since it involves only $\alpha_1 - \alpha_2$, the difference of polarizabilities of the 'equivalent statistical link'.

A knowledge of the value of the stress-optical coefficient for rubber should therefore enable us to calculate $\alpha_1 - \alpha_2$, the anisotropy of the statistical link.

Taking $C = 2 \cdot 33 \times 10^{-4}$ cm.²/kg. (or $2 \cdot 38 \times 10^{-10}$ cm.²/dyne), the slope of the experimental line in Fig. 8.8, the author (Treloar, 1946 b) has calculated in this way the following value of optical anisotropy for the equivalent statistical link:

$$\alpha_1 - \alpha_2 = 5 \cdot 65 \times 10^{-24} \text{ cm.}^3 \tag{8.21}$$

However, an examination of the data of Thibodeau and McPherson (1934) shows that the stress-optical coefficient depends significantly on the type of vulcanization to which the rubber is subjected. For pure rubber-sulphur compounds its value was found to increase linearly with the percentage of combined sulphur, from $2 \cdot 67 \times 10^{-10}$ cm.$^2$/dyne at $2 \cdot 85$ per cent. sulphur to about $3 \cdot 51 \times 10^{-10}$ cm.$^2$/dyne at $6 \cdot 2$ per cent. sulphur. This large dependence on degree of vulcanization suggests that the sulphur itself is modifying either the polarizability or the stiffness (and therefore the length of the equivalent random link) of the polyisoprene molecule, or both. This would not be surprising, particularly if a proportion of the sulphur combines to form cyclic linkages along the chain (cf. Chap. V). This observation indicates that for the derivation of the fundamental optical properties of the polyisoprene chain it would be preferable to choose the value of stress-optical coefficient extrapolated to zero sulphur content. From Thibodeau and McPherson's data this extrapolated value of $C$ is $1 \cdot 96 \times 10^{-4}$ cm.$^2$/dyne, leading to a somewhat lower figure for the anisotropy of the equivalent random link, viz.

$$\alpha_1 - \alpha_2 = 4 \cdot 67 \times 10^{-24} \text{ cm.}^3 \tag{8.22}$$

*Anisotropy of the polyisoprene chain*

Thus far, no indication has been given of the value to be assigned to the 'equivalent random link'. However, this may be obtained indirectly if we can find an independent method of calculating the optical polarizabilities of the polyisoprene chain. Such a calculation would be of considerable interest, since it would lead to an empirical evaluation of the degree of 'kinkiness' or the mean statistical length of the rubber molecule.

The means of calculating the principal polarizabilities of the polyisoprene chain are already available. As Denbigh (1940) has shown, polarizability is an additive property of bonds, the polarizability of a molecule being obtainable from the individual bond polarizabilities. Denbigh has listed the longitudinal and transverse polarizabilities $b_l$ and $b_t$ for a number of bonds, deduced from molecular refractivities and either (1) the Kerr constants or (2) the depolarization of scattered light, for a large

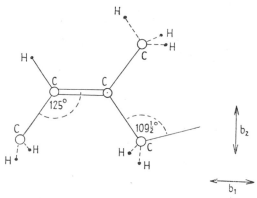

FIG. 8.11. The isoprene unit in the rubber chain (schematic). The bonds represented by dotted lines are not in the plane of the paper.

number of molecules. Details of the method of calculating the molecular polarizabilities from the bond polarizabilities will be found in his paper.

For the polyisoprene (rubber) chain (Fig. 8.11) the required bond polarizabilities are given below:

| Bond | $b_l \times 10^{25}$ cm.$^3$ | $b_t \times 10^{25}$ cm.$^3$ |
|------|------|------|
| C—C | 18·8 | 0·2 |
| C=C | 28·6 | 10·6 |
| C—H | 7·9 | 5·8 |

From these the author† has calculated the three principal polarizabilities, per isoprene unit, assuming the molecule to have the planar configuration shown in Fig. 8.11, and assuming the values of valence angles as shown therein. Of these three polarizabilities $b_1$ refers to the direction of the chain length, $b_2$ to the perpendicular direction, in the plane of the molecule,

† Treloar, unpublished work.

and $b_3$ to the direction normal to this plane. The result, per isoprene unit, is

$$b_1 = 11{\cdot}47 \times 10^{-24} \text{ cm.}^3$$

$$b_2 = 10{\cdot}17 \times 10^{-24} \text{ cm.}^3$$

$$b_3 = \phantom{0}6{\cdot}62 \times 10^{-24} \text{ cm.}^3$$

In the problem of strain birefringence we are concerned only with the longitudinal and mean transverse polarizabilities, $b_l$ and $b_t$ which are

$$b_l = b_1 = 11{\cdot}47 \times 10^{-24}$$

$$b_t = \tfrac{1}{2}(b_2 + b_3) = 8{\cdot}39 \times 10^{-24}. \tag{8.23}$$

The optical anisotropy, per isoprene unit, is therefore

$$b_l - b_t = 3{\cdot}08 \times 10^{-24}. \tag{8.24}$$

Comparing this with the experimental figure for $\alpha_1 - \alpha_2$, namely $4{\cdot}67 \times 10^{-24}$ (8.22), it follows that one random link is the optical equivalent of $4{\cdot}67/3{\cdot}08$ or $1{\cdot}52$ isoprene units.

This figure is intermediate between the figure obtained on the assumption of free rotation about single bonds, with no mutual interference between atoms, namely $0{\cdot}7$ isoprene units per random link, and that calculated by W. Kuhn and H. Kuhn, from flow-birefringence and viscosity data, namely $2{\cdot}8$ isoprene units per random link.

The significance of the equivalent statistical link from the standpoint of the degree of kinkiness or mean statistical length of the molecule has already been discussed in Chapter VI (p. 110). The present figure rests on a more direct quantitative basis than that of W. Kuhn and H. Kuhn, and is probably a more reliable estimate of this important quantity.

## 6. General conclusions

From the foregoing account it is apparent that the subject of the analysis of strain-birefringence in rubber is of very fundamental importance in throwing light on the molecular structure of vulcanized rubber. Not only is it possible to derive comparatively simple laws for the dependence of the birefringence on the principal stresses and principal strains, which are in good agreement with experimental observations, but also important information may be obtained on the flexibility of the molecules themselves. In addition, as we shall see in more detail in the following chapters, information may be obtained on the development of crystallization as an accompaniment of the strain, when the conditions are suitable.

# CHAPTER IX

## CRYSTALLIZATION IN STRETCHED AND UNSTRETCHED RUBBER†

### 1. Introduction

THE subject of crystallization in rubbers, already touched on in Chapter I, is not only a very wide one, but is also one which has a bearing on very many properties of scientific and technical importance. The most fundamental source of information, and that by which the phenomenon was first demonstrated by Katz (1925), is the X-ray diffraction technique, and from this most of our knowledge concerning the quantity and orientation of crystalline material, and the structure of the crystallites has been, and is likely to continue to be, provided. However, for many purposes the interest is mainly in relative, as distinct from absolute, measurements of the degree or state of crystallization, and in such investigations other methods, such as the measurement of density changes or optical double refraction, may be more convenient. In the present chapter we shall endeavour to bring together the knowledge derived from these various independent sources and to discuss the principal phenomena of crystallization in both raw and vulcanized rubber. The effect of crystallization on the mechanical properties of rubber will be discussed in the chapter following.

The very existence of crystallization, and particularly of a species of crystallization which can be brought about by stretching, and which disappears on removal of the tension, may seem at first sight a somewhat difficult conception to accept, and there are, of course, important differences between crystallization in rubbers and polymers and crystallization in low-molecular compounds. These differences arise from the fact that in polymeric materials the crystals are not separable as a distinct phase, but are intimately bound up with the structure, as

† In preparing this chapter advantage has been taken of the excellent survey of crystallization phenomena in rubbers by Wood, *Advances in Colloid Science*, *II* (Interscience Publishers, New York, 1946).

illustrated in Fig. 1.3. The essential criterion of crystallization is the internal regularity of the atomic arrangement; in this respect, the X-ray diffraction pattern is itself sufficient evidence for the existence of a crystalline structure, though the crystallization is only partial, and the crystallites are generally very small. The examination of the course of crystallization under a variety of conditions has led to a satisfactory qualitative understanding of the process of crystallization in stretched and unstretched rubbers, but we are not yet within sight of a detailed theory which will account for the various observed phenomena in a quantitative sense.

## 2. The structure and size of the crystallites

The X-ray diffraction technique may in principle be used to obtain information on the size of the crystallites, and also on the structure of the crystal, that is to say, on the precise arrangement of atoms in the crystal lattice. For the structure analysis it is essential to work with stretched rubber, and thus to obtain the advantage of the degree of order thereby introduced. Even so, conditions are less advantageous than in the case of a single crystal, for, though the crystallites are alined with respect to one dimension (the fibre axis), there is a random orientation with respect to the other two dimensions. In addition the small size of the crystallites leads to a broadening of the spots in the diffraction pattern, while the presence of the 'amorphous' background further increases the difficulty of measuring a sufficiently large number of spot positions and intensities.

The problem of structure analysis normally proceeds by the following stages: (1) the determination of the unit cell from measurements of spot positions; (2) the postulation of a hypothetical structure, for which the spot intensities may be calculated by Fourier transformation; and (3) comparison of calculated and experimental intensities. If the calculated and experimental intensities agree, the hypothetical structure is assumed correct; if not, the calculations must be repeated for other hypothetical structures until agreement is obtained.

In the postulation of a structure use may be made of any available evidence from chemical or other sources which may be of assistance. Thus, for example, it is clear that the long-chain molecules must run through the unit cell in the general direction of the stretched length of the rubber. Also, the number and order of succession of the atoms in the molecular chain is known, and also the approximate distances between them. By such means as these, problems which might well be insoluble if their examination were related exclusively to X-ray data may be brought within the scope of structure analysis.

### Unit cell dimensions

The first question—the determination of the unit cell of the rubber crystal—has, unfortunately, not yet been unambiguously decided. Different workers have suggested that the unit cell is either ortho-rhombic, that is, having three unequal but mutually perpendicular edges, or monoclinic. In the monoclinic system two edges include an angle $\beta$ differing from 90°, while the third is at right angles to both. The differences between these various proposed cells are actually not great, and the estimated values of $\beta$ differ only slightly from 90°. The most recent work of Bunn (1942) gives the following as the most probable dimensions of the edges of the unit cell, in Angstrom units:

$$a = 12 \cdot 46; \qquad b = 8 \cdot 89$$

$$c \text{ (fibre axis)} = 8 \cdot 10; \qquad \beta = 92°.$$

The angle $\beta$ is that between the $b$ and $c$ axes. The proposed cell contains 4 molecular chains and 8 isoprene units; it gives a density (calculated from the absolute atomic weights) of $1 \cdot 00$.

### Molecular configuration in the crystal

Our knowledge of the detailed structure, i.e. of the precise configurations of the molecules in the unit cell, is still far from precise. The repeating unit along the axis of the chain, $8 \cdot 10$ A, is not long enough to accommodate the fully extended molecule in the planar form shown in Fig. 1.2, hence the molecule must be 'bent' or distorted out of the plane in some way. In the structures proposed by Bunn (1942) for both rubber and its *trans*-isomer gutta-percha, the single bonds adjacent to the double bond, as well as the methyl group, are distorted considerably out of the plane. This solution, which appears improbable on *a priori* grounds, has not been generally accepted. Jeffrey (1944) has shown that Bunn's data for gutta-percha may be fitted equally well by an alternative structure not involving distortion of the doubly-bonded unit from the normal planar arrangement, the overall shortening being obtained by a suitable rotation about the single bond connecting successive isoprene units. Jeffrey therefore concludes that Bunn has not established the validity of his structural interpretation, and that the available experimental evidence on which his conclusions were based was not sufficient to provide an unambiguous solution to the problem.

*Electron diffraction*

Further evidence which has a bearing on the problem of the molecular configuration in the crystal, and which seems to lend support to Jeffrey's criticisms, is provided by the recent electron diffraction work of Fisher (1948). While using a unit cell differing only very slightly from Bunn's, Fisher postulates a planar configuration of the isoprene units, and assumes only normal bond lengths and valence angles, i.e. $C—C = 1.54$ A; $C{=}C = 1.33$ A; angle $C—C—C = 109\frac{1}{2}°$; angle $C—C{=}C = 120°$. The shortening necessary to fit the chain into the repeating distance (which incidentally is given as 8.23 A, compared with the X-ray figure of 8.10 A) is introduced by rotation of the connecting link $C_4—C_6$ (Fig. 9.1) out of the plane of the isoprene groups. Her structure is represented in 'plan' and 'elevation' in the accompanying figure.

This model is applied to the interpretation of the diffuse pattern which appears on the electron diffraction photographs in addition to the normal spot pattern. It is shown that the diffuse pattern arises from the thermal vibrations of the molecules in the crystal lattice, and it is claimed that the proposed structure accounts more satisfactorily for the details of the pattern than does the structure put forward by Bunn.

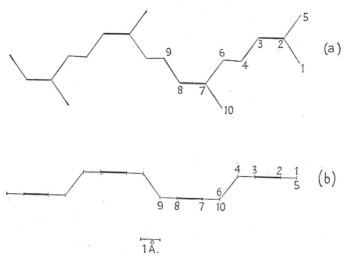

FIG. 9.1. Configuration of molecule in rubber crystal. (Fisher, 1948.) Projections (*a*) in plane of isoprene units, (*b*) perpendicular to plane of isoprene units.

### 'Higher orientation'

When rubber is subjected to a simple elongation, the crystals are alined in one direction only. But if a short wide strip is stretched, the contraction in width is relatively less than the contraction in thickness, and, under this condition, a certain amount of orientation of the other two crystal axes is found to occur. This phenomenon, which has been investigated by Gehman and Field (1939), is usually referred to as a 'higher orientation'. It is revealed by a marked change in the relative intensities of certain spots in the diffraction pattern, which is interpreted as a preferential orientation of the *a*-axes of the unit cell (12·46 A) in the plane of the sheet. Gehman and Field found the degree of higher orientation to increase with increasing ratio of width to length of the stretched sheet. It has been shown in Chapter IV that the stretching of a wide sheet results in a deformation which approximates to a pure shear. Gehman and Field's result therefore means that a pure shear is the most favourable type of strain for the production of higher orientation. This is perhaps not altogether surprising, for in a pure shear the three principal extension ratios (which may be written $\alpha$, 1, $1/\alpha$ respectively) are in geometrical progression; each is therefore as different from both the others as it can possibly be. In a sense, therefore, the pure shear is the most unsymmetrical possible type of homogeneous strain. If the crystallites have any tendency to take on an orientation which is related to the principal strains, we might expect the most favourable condition for three-dimensional orientation to correspond with that type of strain which is the farthest removed from any form of symmetry, i.e. the pure shear.

The possibilities offered by this technique in the analysis of the structure of the crystal may be very important, and have certainly not yet been fully explored. A perfect state of 'higher orientation' would correspond closely in effect to a single crystal; any approach to this state should result in considerable simplification of the interpretation and analysis of the diffraction pattern.

### Size of crystallites

The estimation of the dimensions of the crystallites depends on the broadening of the spots in the diffraction pattern as the crystal dimensions are diminished. The method is applicable only when the dimensions are less than about 1,000 A, and becomes increasingly accurate as the dimensions are reduced. Unfortunately in rubber the dimensions fall near the upper limit and hence are difficult to assess with accuracy. In addition, there may be a broadening due to other factors, such as, for example, imperfections of the crystal lattice, which it is hardly possible to estimate. For these reasons, estimates of the size of crystallites must be regarded as subject to considerable uncertainty.

The original work of Hengstenberg and Mark yielded a value of greater than 600 A in the direction of the fibre axis, with 180 A and 530 A for the dimensions normal respectively to the 020 and 200 planes. More recently Gehman and Field (1944) have given values which varied somewhat with the type of compound, ranging from 52 to 81 A for the 020 dimension and from 268 to 338 A for the 200 dimension. However, the uncertainty was such that an alternative method of estimation gave values two or three times as large. No estimate was given for the dimension parallel to the fibre axis.

## 3. Crystallization in unstretched rubber

### Freezing and melting temperature

It is a familiar fact that raw rubber, when stored in a cool place, gradually becomes hard and relatively inelastic, and at

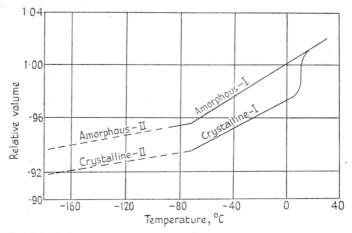

FIG. 9.2. Volume-temperature relationship for purified rubber, showing second-order transition at −72° C., and crystal melting at 11° C. (Bekkedahl, 1934.)

the same time loses its transparency. On heating above a certain temperature, the original state is reproduced. The 'melting' phenomena may conveniently be studied by observing the changes in specific volume (reciprocal density) in a dilatometer, using a confining liquid (e.g. mercury or alcohol) which is not appreciably absorbed by the rubber. Typical volume-temperature curves obtained in this way by Bekkedahl (1934) are shown in Fig. 9.2. The crystalline rubber, represented by the lower of the two curves in this figure, melted in the range 6° to 16° C., with an expansion of volume of about 2·7 per cent.

By contrast, a rubber which was cooled quickly to liquid-air temperature remained amorphous, and showed only the second-order transition at a temperature of $-72°$ C.; the crystalline rubber also showed this transition in addition to the crystalline-amorphous transition.

The temperature range in which melting of the crystals occurs was found by Bekkedahl and Wood (1941 b) to be a function

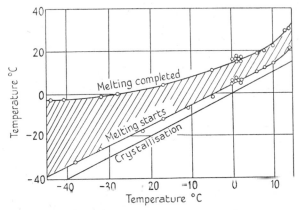

FIG. 9.3.   Melting range of crystalline rubber as function of temperature of crystallization.  (Bekkedahl and Wood, 1941.)

of the temperature at which the crystallization takes place. This relationship is shown in Fig. 9.3. As the temperature of crystallization is lowered, the temperature of melting not only falls but also spreads over a wider range. At temperatures exceeding 15° C. the rate of crystallization is negligibly small. It is interesting to observe that melting commences only when the temperature is from 4° to 6° C. above the temperature of crystallization; there is therefore no temperature at which the crystalline and amorphous components may be regarded as in equilibrium.

Indeed, the fact that the melting temperature depends so markedly on the temperature of crystallization is in itself evidence of the lack of a true equilibrium state. This lack of equilibrium leads to some very curious phenomena, which have been pointed out by Wood (1946). If rubber which has been

crystallized at a temperature of $-30°$ C. is raised to a temperature of $0°$ C., melting of the crystals takes place immediately,
but this is followed by slow crystallization. Hence melting and
crystallization may both take place at one temperature. Also, if
rubber is crystallized at two different temperatures in succession, partial melting will take place over two distinct ranges

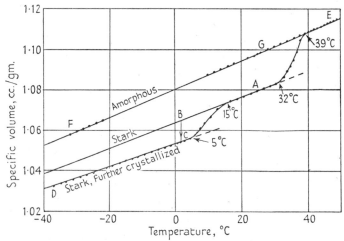

FIG. 9.4. Further crystallization and subsequent melting of 'stark'
rubber. (Wood, 1946.)

of temperature. Wood quotes the case of a 'stark' rubber (i.e.
rubber crystallized by storage) which melted in the temperature
range $32°$ to $39°$ C. If this crystalline rubber was held at $2°$ C.,
further crystallization occurred. On now slowly raising the
temperature, the crystals formed at $2°$ C. melted at the usual
temperature (corresponding to this temperature of crystallization) of $5°$ to $15°$ C., while the crystals originally present, and
presumably formed at a higher temperature, showed a quite
separate melting-range of $32°$ to $39°$ C. (Fig. 9.4).

A rather unexpected result, quoted by Wood (1946), is that
the melting temperature is completely independent of the degree
of crystallization achieved. This was based on experiments at
$2°$ C., in which crystallization was interrupted when the volume
decrease had amounted to $0·085$, $1·0$, and $2·7$ per cent. respectively.

*Effect of hydrostatic pressure*

Thiessen and Kirch (1938, 1939) have shown, by X-ray studies, that the rate of crystallization is increased by the application of hydrostatic pressure (up to about 30 atmospheres), but under very high pressures (8,000 kg./cm.$^2$) Dow (1939) found no crystallization at 0° C., which was explained by the presumed increase in viscosity of the amorphous rubber under

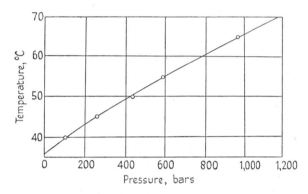

Fig. 9.5. Effect of pressure on melting temperature of 'stark' rubber. (Wood, Bekkedahl, and Gibson, 1945.) (1 bar = 750 mm.)

these conditions. Under equilibrium conditions increase of pressure should favour the crystalline state, but the accompanying increase in viscosity at the same time greatly increases the time required for the attainment of equilibrium. If, however, a crystalline rubber is subjected to pressure, the melting temperature is raised, and at 1,270 kg./cm.$^2$ Dow observed a melting temperature as high as 77·5° C. for a rubber which had been crystallized at atmospheric pressure. A more systematic investigation of the variation of melting temperature (determined from disappearance of birefringence) with applied pressure, carried out by Wood, Bekkedahl, and Gibson (1945), yielded the results shown in Fig. 9.5. These experiments were performed on 'stark' rubber, whose (mean) melting temperature at atmospheric pressure was 36·2° C.; the figures are applicable only to this particular rubber, since the melting temperature depends not only on the temperature of crystallization but also on the pressure applied during crystallization. The curve of Fig. 9.5 could be represented by the equation

$$\log_{10}(p+1300) = 5 \cdot 9428 - 875/T, \qquad (9.1)$$

where $T$ is measured in degrees Kelvin and $p$ in kg./cm.$^2$ Differentiation of this equation gives

$$\frac{dT}{dp} = \frac{T^2}{2,015(p+1300)}. \qquad (9.1\,a)$$

The Clapeyron equation for the variation of melting-point with temperature is

$$\frac{dp}{dT} = \frac{L}{T \cdot \Delta V}, \qquad (9.2)$$

where $L$ is the latent heat of crystallization and $\Delta V$ the corresponding volume change. Hence, from $(9.1\,a)$ it is possible (assuming this equation to be applicable)† to calculate $L/\Delta V$. At atmospheric pressure the value of $L/\Delta V$ thus obtained was 846 joules/cm.$^3$, which with the measured value of $\Delta V$ ($0 \cdot 0191$ cm.$^3$/gm.) gave for the latent heat for this particular sample $16 \cdot 2$ joules/gm. or $3 \cdot 87$ cals./gm. It should be remembered, however, that the rubber is not fully crystallized, and that this figure is therefore the latent heat for partial crystallization, which may be very different from the true latent heat of crystallization (see below).

### Rate of crystallization

A number of investigations have been concerned with the examination of the rate of crystallization of unstretched rubber. Using the dilatometric method Bekkedahl (1934) studied the changes in specific volume of raw rubber at 0° C., obtaining the characteristic S-shaped curve of Fig. 9.6. Crystallization is at first extremely slow, but the rate later accelerates, finally becoming slower again as the time increases. The rate of crystallization varies also with temperature; at 0° C. the process is substantially complete in about 10 days, but with reduction of temperature the rate increases to a maximum at −25° C., then falls again, until at temperatures below −50° C. it becomes too small to observe. At −25° C. crystallization is complete

† See p. 176 on the question of thermodynamic equilibrium.

in a few hours. The slowing down at lower temperatures is attributed to the increase in internal viscosity of the rubber, i.e. to the reduction in the mobility of the chains.

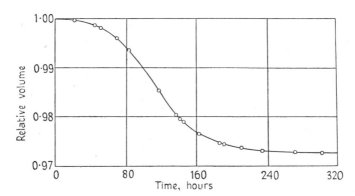

FIG. 9.6. The growth of crystallization at 0° C., measured by volume changes. (Bekkedahl, 1934.)

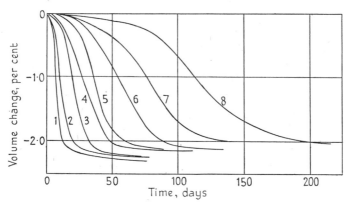

FIG. 9.7. Dependence of rate of crystallization at 2° C. on combined sulphur content. (Bekkedahl and Wood, 1941.) (1) 0·0 and 0·1 per cent. S. (2) 0·20 per cent. S. (3) 0·30 per cent. S. (4) 0·35 per cent. S. (5) 0·40 per cent. S. (6) 0·43 per cent. S. (7) 0·46 per cent. S. (8) 0·50 per cent. S.

Vulcanized rubber also crystallizes in a similar manner to raw rubber, but the rate of crystallization becomes slower as the percentage of combined sulphur is increased. This is illustrated in Fig. 9.7, taken from Bekkedahl and Wood's paper (Bekkedahl and Wood, 1941 a). Curiously, however, the melting curve was completely unaffected, either in range or position, by the vulcanization. This was true both for plain rubber-sulphur compounds and for compounds containing an accelerator.

## 4. Crystallization in stretched rubber

The phenomena encountered in stretched rubber are in many respects comparable with the effects in the unstretched state. The chief differences are the increased rapidity of crystalliza-tion, the orientation of the crystallites, and the close connexion between the state of crystallization and the mechanical strain.

With raw rubber at room temperature the characteristic spots in the X-ray diffraction pattern begin to appear in the region of 200 to 300 per cent. elongation, and increase in intensity, at the expense of the amorphous halo, as the extension is increased. The fact that the spots are only slightly drawn out, or elongated, at the lower extensions proves that the crystallites are formed preferentially with their axes parallel to the direc-tion of extension, in contrast to the crystallites resulting from the freezing of unstretched rubber, which are oriented at ran-dom, giving rise to the ring pattern characteristic of a crystalline powder (Debye–Scherrer pattern). Gehman and Field (1939) observed, however, that by freezing rubber under extensions of less than 100 per cent., patterns in which the spots were greatly elongated, forming arcs of circles, could be obtained. These patterns represented a state intermediate between an alined and a random orientation. Moreover, on freezing a rubber stretched to an intermediate extension the spots tended to elongate, showing that the crystals formed in the subsequent freezing were less well oriented than those formed immediately after extension.

### Rate of crystallization

The progress of crystallization in stretched raw rubber has been followed by the author, by observation of the accompany-ing birefringence and density changes (Treloar, 1941). Fig. 9.9 shows the changes in birefringence observed when the rubber was stretched quickly at 0° C. to various extensions, and main-tained at that temperature until crystallization had been

completed. At low extensions these curves have a similar
S-shape to the crystallization curve for unstretched rubber
(Fig. 9.6), but with the time-scale becoming more and more contracted with increasing extension. At the higher extensions the
rate of crystallization is so rapid that only the last portion of the

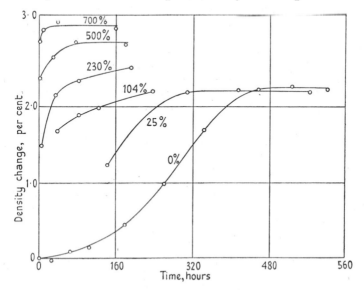

Fig. 9.8. Density changes in raw rubber at various extensions at 0° C.

curve is susceptible to observation. The natural inference from
these observations is that the process of crystallization is essentially the same, whether the rubber is stretched or unstretched,
but that the rate at which it takes place varies enormously with
the applied strain.

There is some doubt as to the extent to which the birefringence
may be assumed to represent the relative amount of crystallization. At very low extensions, where the crystals are imperfectly
oriented, it certainly fails, while at very high extensions there
will be a contribution due to the strain-birefringence of the
amorphous component of the rubber to be taken into account.
With this in mind, comparable investigations were carried out
by the density method. These yielded the results shown in
Fig. 9.8, which confirm in all essentials the conclusions drawn

from the birefringence studies. Between 100 per cent. and 700 per cent. extension the density changes were, in fact, almost exactly proportional to the birefringence; it was only below 100 per cent. extension that a significant discrepancy was observed.

At higher temperatures the equilibrium crystallization is

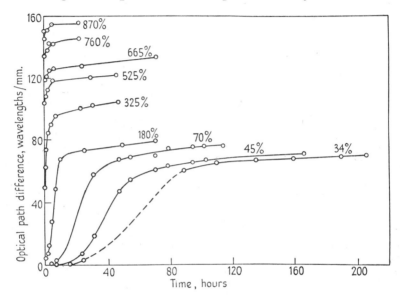

Fig. 9.9. Changes in birefringence in raw rubber at various extensions at 0° C.

achieved still more rapidly. Thus at 25° C. birefringence studies showed that crystallization was apparently almost completed within a very short time after extension, and it was only possible to observe a slight subsequent increase, while at 50° C. the final state appeared to be attained within the time required to make an observation, i.e. a few seconds.

*The melting temperature*

If raw rubber is stretched to a very high extension, the crystallization is sufficient to maintain the strained state even when the stretching force is removed. Rubber brought into this highly oriented state has sometimes been called 'racked rubber'. If the temperature of highly oriented crystalline rubber is slowly raised, retraction to the original unstrained state is found to occur at a certain well-defined temperature, which may be regarded as the melting-point of the crystals. This melting-point, while not much dependent on the amount of extension, does depend on the temperature at which the stretching is carried out (Treloar, 1940).

A similar phenomenon is encountered with vulcanized rubber, but in this case the melting temperature of the crystals is usually below room temperature and is not so sharply defined. Gibbons, Gerke, and Tingey (1933) found the melting or retraction temperature to decrease regularly with increase in combined sulphur. A test based on this property (the 'T-50' test) has been used for rapid evaluation of the efficiency of vulcanization.

### Dependence of crystallization on elongation and temperature

The fact that in either raw or vulcanized rubber the crystals formed on stretching disappear entirely within a rather narrow temperature range, when there is no applied tension, does not mean that a similar disappearance would occur if the tension were maintained. Under such conditions, the crystals melt only gradually. This has been shown, for example, by Thiessen and Wittstadt's experiments on vulcanized rubber (Thiessen and Wittstadt, 1938), and has been confirmed in numerous independent investigations. In Field's experiments (Field, 1941), the amount of crystallization at constant extension appeared to be a linear function of the temperature, over the range 30° to 90° C. At the latter temperature there was still considerable crystallization at the higher elongations. In this case, therefore, there is certainly no sharp melting-point, but a very wide range of temperature in which crystalline and amorphous phases may coexist, and the apparently sharp melting-point of racked rubber must be due to the fact that the melting is assisted by the tendency of the extended molecules to retract—a tendency which is neutralized by the applied tension when the rubber is held in the extended state.

The author has studied the variation of birefringence with

extension, at a number of temperatures, using both raw and vulcanized rubber. Fig. 9.10 shows the curves obtained for raw rubber, at two different temperatures (Treloar, 1941). These figures refer to samples which had been held at a particular extension for one hour (after quick stretching); each point on the curves therefore represents a different sample of rubber.

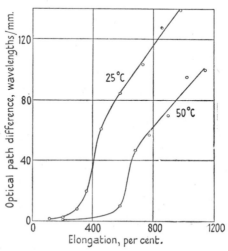

FIG. 9.10. Birefringence in raw rubber as function of elongation.

This procedure was adopted because of the effects of flow, which varies in a complicated way with increasing extension (see below). Taking the birefringence to be proportional to the amount of crystallization, it is seen that crystallization sets in rather suddenly at a certain elongation, after which it increases more slowly up to the maximum extension which could be applied. The elongation at which crystallization starts rises with increasing temperature, as would be expected.

Rather similar effects, some of which have been referred to in the preceding chapter, are observed with vulcanized rubber. Fig. 9.11 shows the variation of birefringence with elongation ratio $\alpha$, for a vulcanized rubber, at various temperatures (Treloar, 1947 b). The solid line is the theoretical strain-birefringence curve, which is fitted to the experimental data for low elongations, i.e. in the absence of crystallization. At 100° C. there is evidence of only slight crystallization, but as the temperature is lowered, down to $-25°$ C., the experimental curves deviate from the theoretical at successively lower elongations, and at the same time the maximum birefringence rises to higher values. These differences between the theoretical and experimental

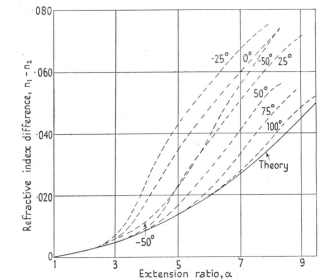

FIG. 9.11. Birefringence in vulcanized rubber as function of elongation at various temperatures (°C.), compared with theoretical relation

$$n_1 - n_2 = C(\alpha^2 - 1/\alpha).$$

curves are related to the amount of crystallization. It is interesting to observe the anomalous course of the curve at $-50°$ C., which shows apparently less crystallization than at either $-25°$ or $0°$ C. This is in harmony with the behaviour of unstretched rubber, which, as we have already seen, shows a reduction in rate of crystallization when the temperature is reduced below $-25°$ C.

As shown in the preceding chapter, crystallization gives rise to large hysteresis effects. The curves of Fig. 9.11 therefore are not reversible, and do not represent equilibrium states. Nor do they permit of a quantitative estimation of the percentages of crystallinity, since the birefringence to be expected at 100 per cent. crystallization is not known.

## 5. Absolute determination of percentage crystallinity

The only absolute method of determining the proportion of crystalline matter present in either stretched or unstretched rubber is by measurement of the intensity of the X-ray diffraction pattern. Work on this problem has been carried out in recent years by Field (1941) and by Goppel (1946). The X-ray pattern of stretched crystalline rubber contains an array of spots superimposed on an amorphous 'halo' or diffuse ring. Field's method was to compare the intensity of this amorphous halo, in the crystalline rubber, with the corresponding intensity for an unstretched, uncrystalline rubber. The ratio gives immediately the proportion of amorphous rubber in the mixed system and, by difference, the proportion of crystallinity. If at the same time the relative intensities of a particular crystal diffraction spot and of the amorphous halo were measured (over a range of extension), this ratio could be used subsequently as a more convenient means of arriving at the proportion of crystallinity, but it is based on the prior measurement of the relative intensities of the amorphous halo.

Typical figures taken from Field's results are shown in Fig. 9.12. For both raw and vulcanized rubber, crystallization starts in the region 200 to 300 per cent. extension, and reaches a maximum in the neighbourhood of 80 per cent. crystallization. More recently, Gehman and Field (1944) have shown that the degree of crystallinity increases with increasing molecular weight of the rubber before vulcanization, and have obtained up to 90 per cent. crystallinity for particular compounds.

These X-ray data of Field confirm the qualitative evidence provided by birefringence and density studies, and have, of course, the additional advantage of giving absolute values. On this question, however, Goppel (1946) has produced conflicting evidence. He finds apparently much lower figures for the proportion of crystallinity, which throw doubt on the quantitative reliability of Field's results. Though Goppel used essentially the same principle as Field, he claims to have eliminated possible errors, arising for example from variations in intensity of the incident beam, variations in development of the photographs, and the effect of scattered radiation. The chief modification which Goppel introduced was the inclusion of a standard inorganic powder which was exposed to the X-ray beam at the same time, giving a photograph on the same film, thus providing a standard for comparison in the intensity

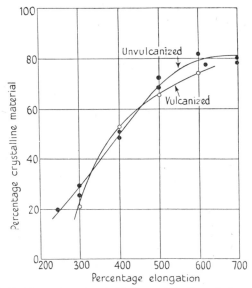

FIG. 9.12. Percentage crystallinity as function of elongation in raw and vulcanized rubber. (Field, 1941.)

measurements, and eliminating the sources of error referred to. Goppel's result, for a vulcanized rubber without fillers, is shown in Fig. 9.13. The maximum crystallization which he was able to obtain was 29 per cent., at an extension of 550 per cent.

Goppel also measured the percentage crystallinity in 'stark' rubber which had been stored for varying numbers of years. This percentage ranged from 10 to 15 per cent. for times of storage of between 5 and 10 years up to 20 to 25 per cent. for a storage time of 30 years.

In view of these discordant results, it is clearly desirable that further investigations should be carried out on this question. In X-ray intensity measurements it is obviously difficult to achieve the required accuracy, and an independent line of approach would be highly advantageous. Such an independent approach would become available if the dimensions of the unit cell of the rubber crystal could be determined with certainty by X-ray methods, for it would then be possible to calculate the density of the crystal. If this were known, it would then be possible to make use of density measurements, which can easily be carried out with the necessary accuracy, for the determination of the percentage crystallinity. The most reliable estimate of the density of the rubber crystal is probably that of Bunn (1942), who obtained a figure of 1·00. Unfortunately the temperature to which this refers is not specified. This is rather an important omission, since the density varies by 1 per cent. for a change of temperature of 15° C. Assuming it to refer to a temperature of 20° C., the X-ray density would be 10·0 per cent. higher than the density of purified amorphous rubber,

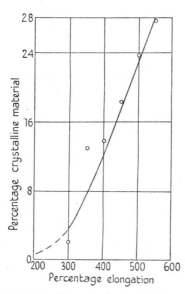

FIG. 9.13. Percentage crystallinity as function of elongation in vulcanized rubber. (Goppel, 1946.)

which from McPherson's data is 0·909 at 20° C. (McPherson, 1932). On this basis the density change which would correspond to 100 per cent. crystallization is therefore 10·0 per cent., calculated on the density in the amorphous state. Experimentally, a typical figure for the density increase on freezing at 0° C. is 2·7 per cent. (Bekkedahl, 1934), which would therefore correspond to only 27 per cent. crystallization. This figure is comparable with Goppel's estimate for stark rubber. The figures for stretched crystalline rubber are somewhat higher. The author (Treloar, 1941) measured a density change of just over 3 per cent. in raw rubber at 700 per cent. extension, and estimated from birefringence measurements that the maximum crystallization obtained would correspond to a density change of 3·75 per cent., which would be equivalent to 37·5 per cent. crystallization. However, this figure is probably an over-estimate, since the contribution of the strain birefringence was not taken into account. These figures for raw rubber extended at 0° C. are not strictly comparable with Goppel's figures for vulcanized rubber at room temperature, but so far as they go, they tend to confirm the accuracy of his data, and to suggest that the maximum possible crystallinity is nearer to 30 than to 90 per cent.

It is interesting to compare these estimates with figures for the degree of crystallinity in unstretched polyethylene obtained by two independent methods. Polyethylene possesses the advantage over rubber that the X-ray density has been definitely determined, and is given by Bunn (1939) as 1·00, so that density measurements on the mixed system may be used to derive fairly reliable estimates of the degree of crystallinity. In this way Hunter and Oakes (1945) estimated the percentage crystallinity at 55 per cent. over the range of temperature from 0° to 70° C. Above 70° C. the ratio began to fall, the rate of fall becoming increasingly rapid as the melting-point (115° C.) was approached. An alternative method, by Raine, Richards, and Ryder (1945), made use of measurements of heat content, in conjunction with the known latent heat of fusion of lower-molecular paraffins. This method, which was probably less reliable than the density method, gave a rather higher estimate of crystallinity, 75 per cent. at room temperature.

In considering these figures it must be remembered that polyethylene crystallizes with great ease, and at a comparatively high temperature. The factors of both packing and internal mobility of the amorphous material would be expected to favour a higher proportion of crystallinity than in the case of rubber. In this sense, Hunter and Oakes's figure of 55 per cent. crystallinity, which is about twice that estimated by Goppel for unstretched fully crystallized raw rubber, fits nicely into the general picture.

## 6. The mechanism of crystallization

The most significant phenomena of crystallization in rubbers, which must be taken into account in any attempt to formulate a theory of crystallization, would seem to be (1) the characteristic S-shape of the curve of crystal growth; (2) the existence of an unsharp melting-point; (3) the fact that the melting temperature is a function of the temperature of crystallization, but is independent of degree of crystallization or state of vulcanization; and (4) the relation between degree of crystallization and extension.

It must be said at once that a comprehensive theory of crystallization which would account quantitatively for these main effects has not yet been evolved. This section will therefore be concerned mainly with discussing in a rather general qualitative manner the nature of the problem, and with indicating possible lines of advance.

There is now general agreement that the shape of the crystal growth curves shown in Figs. 9.8 and 9.9 is explicable on the basis of the initial formation of nuclei. These nuclei are considered to arise spontaneously, from chance fluctuations of the state of local order. Once established they persist, and further crystallization is more likely to take place by accretion about the already formed nuclei than by the formation of further nuclei, though the latter process is not necessarily excluded. As the surface area of the nuclei increases, the rate of crystallization also increases. At a certain stage, however, neighbouring centres of crystallization will begin to encroach on one another, and the freedom of movement of chains will become progressively more and more restricted. Thus, when a certain degree of crystallization has been reached the rate will again slow down, until eventually further crystallization almost ceases, even though there may still be a considerable proportion of uncrystallized material present. Crystallization is known to occur in this way in a large number of substances, whether homogeneous or in solution, and has formed the subject of extensive studies, particularly by Tammann. The rate of crystallization is determined by two factors, of which the first represents the rate of formation of nuclei, and the second the rate of condensation on the surface of nuclei, or 'linear crystallization velocity'. Each of these factors is strongly temperature-dependent. A reduction of temperature favours the crystalline state, but at the same time reduces the molecular mobility, and this tends to reduce the rate at which the transition to the crystalline state occurs. Consequently, as the temperature is reduced, the rate of crystallization first accelerates and then slows down again. In natural rubber the maximum occurs at about −25° C. This is an overall rate, and does not distinguish between the two processes—rate of nuclei formation, and linear crystallization velocity. In general, these processes reach their maximum rates at different temperatures. Thus, for example, a study of glycerol by Tammann and Jenckel (1930) yielded a maximum linear crystallization velocity at −3·5° C., whereas the maximum rate of formation of nuclei was at about −60° C., at which temperature further crystal growth was completely inhibited. It is not possible, with the available data for rubber, to draw conclusions regarding the separate rates of nuclei formation and crystal growth.

Visual evidence for the existence of nuclei seems to be provided by the examination of thin films of crystalline polymers in polarized light. Patterns obtained in this way have been given by Bunn and Alcock (1945), who worked with polyethylene (see frontispiece), and by Smith and Saylor (1939), who studied natural rubber and obtained an exactly similar effect. From these patterns it is clear that the crystallization has proceeded from a central point and spread outwards until the growth from a neighbouring nucleus has been encountered. The issue is not entirely simple, however, because the domains associated with a particular nucleus represent not single crystals but clusters symmetrically disposed about a centre. Moreover, the sign of the double refraction shows the fibre axis to be in the plane of the film, but *at right angles* to the radius joining any given point to the centre of the spherulitic cluster; in other words, the molecules are disposed circumferentially and not radially with respect to the central nucleus. How these clusters develop is not clear; it is possible that the change in density or local orientation accompanying the formation of a crystallite induces a strain in the surrounding medium which enhances the probability of the formation of further crystallites in its immediate vicinity; but this is pure speculation.

While the observed variations of rate of crystallization may thus be fairly satisfactorily interpreted on the basis of the conception of the formation of nuclei, the question of the equilibrium amount of crystallization to be expected under given conditions is less easy to answer. The difference of temperature between crystallization and the beginning of melting (Fig. 9.3) and hysteresis effects generally (e.g. as revealed in birefringence studies) show that in practice a genuine equilibrium of the system as a whole may never be achieved. This makes the application of straightforward thermodynamic reasoning rather difficult. Gee (1947) has argued in favour of the consideration of a partial or relative equilibrium with respect to changes taking place relatively quickly, which may be treated thermodynamically (at least in principle) provided that other changes take place so slowly that their possible existence may be ignored. We have already had an example of this kind of approach in Wood and Roth's work on the stress-temperature relations of rubber (Chap. II) in which an apparent equilibrium was established with respect to changes in temperature provided that the temperature of relaxation was not exceeded. On the same basis Gee considers that in a crystalline rubber at any instant the individual crystallite is in approximate equilibrium with the amorphous rubber in its immediate environment. The point of equilibrium is dependent on the local stresses, which in turn are a function of the local configurations and mutual entanglements of the amorphous parts of the chains. With the lapse of time, changes of a viscous character may lead to rearrangements which are more favourable to further crystal growth, or the tensions in the amorphous chains set up by the crystal growth may be slowly relaxed. This slow relaxation will lead to a gradual shift in the instantaneous point of equilibrium. Ultimately, however, the interconnexions between the various crystalline and amorphous regions may become so numerous and complex that the probability of any further rearrangements leading to a higher state of crystallization becomes vanishingly small. Since the individual crystallite is nearly in equilibrium at any stage of the process of crystallization, a rise of temperature of a few degrees will lead to some melting, and, since melting (unlike crystallization) involves no bulk transport of matter, or molecular diffusion, it will take place in a very short time. The local tensions in the amorphous chains may be expected to depend on the temperature of crystallization, but not on the size of the crystallite; hence on this basis a qualitative explanation of the dependence of melting temperature on temperature of crystallization, but not on the amount of crystallization, seems to be possible.

An extension of these conceptions may provide a basis for the understanding of the crystallization which takes place on elongation. By reducing the entropy of the amorphous component, an extension leads to a shift of the equilibrium point in favour of the crystalline phase, i.e. to a rise in melting temperature. A formal thermodynamic relation may be derived (Gee, 1947) between tensile force and melting temperature. This, which is analogous to the Clausius–Clapeyron relation, contains as parameters the latent heat of fusion and the increase in length accompanying the melting, but since the latter quantity is itself an unknown function of the extension, it cannot at present be employed in a quantitative manner.

For the further development of the theory of crystallization it is necessary to go beyond general thermodynamic considerations, and to work on the basis of a specific physical model, which could be treated by statistical methods. Some progress in this direction has been made, for example by Flory (1947), but it would take us too far to attempt to discuss these developments in detail.

# CHAPTER X

# CRYSTALLIZATION AND MECHANICAL PROPERTIES

## 1. Crystallites as intermolecular linkages

FROM the general structural model represented in Fig. 1.3 and discussed in more detail in the preceding chapter, it is to be expected that the incidence of crystallization should give rise to important changes in mechanical properties. We have already seen (Chap. IV) that the modulus of a rubber in the amorphous state is determined by the number of effective cross-linkages between chains. The formation of crystal nuclei is equivalent, from the mechanical standpoint, to the introduction of additional cross-linkages, having a certain degree of stability or permanence, and this will increase the modulus or hardness of the rubber. With further crystal growth the number of chains involved in any one crystallite may increase to 100 or 1,000, and the crystalline matter may occupy a volume comparable with that taken up by the amorphous component. Under these conditions, the modification of physical properties is profound, the final state bearing little resemblance to that of an amorphous or rubber-like material.

If raw rubber is crystallized in the highly extended state, the oriented crystallites confer on the rubber markedly anisotropic properties. This mechanical anisotropy was the subject of early investigations by Hock (1925), who compared the types of fracture exhibited when both unstretched amorphous rubber and 'racked' or highly oriented crystalline rubber were subjected to quick cooling in liquid air and hammered. The amorphous rubber was found to give typical conchoidal or glass-like fractures, while the oriented material split up in a manner resembling a bundle of fibres, the length of the fibres being parallel to the direction of extension. This fibrous structure may also be demonstrated in racked rubber at room temperature, which may easily be torn into strips in the direction of the extension, though possessing extreme resistance to cutting

or tearing in directions at right angles thereto. Oriented crystalline rubber is in fact closely similar in structure and properties
to natural cellulose fibres, and also to certain highly oriented
synthetic textile fibres, of which nylon is one of the best-known
examples.

Evidence of the reduction in molecular mobility brought
about by the cross-linking action of the crystallites is provided

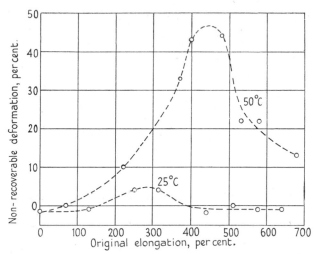

— Fig. 10.1. Plastic flow in raw rubber. Non-recoverable or plastic
deformation plotted against original elongation.

by a number of different observations. One instance of this
effect was demonstrated by the author (Treloar, 1940), who
studied the residual or plastic deformation accompanying the
extension of raw rubber. Strips of raw rubber were stretched
to predetermined lengths for one hour, then released and subjected to relaxation until there was no further contraction.
The residual deformation, when plotted against the initial
elongation, showed a maximum in the intermediate range of
extension (Fig. 10.1). At higher elongations the flow was reduced by crystallization, even though the stress was increasing.
The higher the temperature, the higher was the elongation
required to initiate crystallization, and the higher the position
of the maximum flow.

This observation enables us to understand how raw rubber is able to sustain large elastic deformations, though not possessing any chemical intermolecular linkages. At low elongations the intermolecular cohesions and entanglements provide the necessary resistance to plastic deformation. At higher stresses when these cohesional mechanisms become insufficient by themselves to prevent considerable slippage, crystallization takes over their function. Since the amount of crystallization increases progressively with the stress, the tendency to increased flow is thus automatically compensated.

The onset of crystallization in raw rubber is a rather critical phenomenon. If crystallization succeeds in starting, its further increase with increasing extension is assured, but, if it fails to start at moderate elongations, further extension may result only in increased flow, and crystallization may not occur at all. In the former case the maximum stress which can be applied may become very high, approaching that for a vulcanized rubber, while in the latter case it will remain quite low. Rubber of low molecular weight, obtained by milling or fractionation (Gee and Treloar, 1940), may show little if any crystallization on stretching at room temperature; the same result is achieved by stretching ordinary high-molecular rubber very slowly (thus allowing time for slippage or flow) or by raising the temperature. Similarly, synthetic rubbers which do not crystallize, like GR-S, are generally very weak in the unvulcanized state. The remarkably high elastic extensibility and tensile strength of raw natural rubber is therefore not due wholly, or even primarily, to the entanglement-cohesions between molecules. These cohesions only serve to maintain the structure up to the point where crystallization starts; thereafter, the structure is effectively bound up with the crystalline linkages.

From X-ray observations Gehman and Field (1939) have concluded that when rubber is stretched the crystal nuclei are formed preferentially in the direction of the extension. A similar conclusion was drawn by the author (Treloar, 1941) from a study of the changes in birefringence accompanying crystallization. If this is so, the growth of the crystallites will lead to an increase in the average orientation of the molecular chains. This may explain the curious phenomenon reported by Smith and Saylor (1938) and by Park (1939). These authors observed that when raw rubber is held at an elongation of about 200 or 300 per cent., at a low temperature, the slow crystallization is accompanied by an increase in length, amounting to as much as 4 per cent. of the (stretched) length of the specimen. This must mean that the rotation of the amorphous chains into the direction of the crystallites is sufficiently important first to reduce the tension in the rubber to zero, and then to cause a further extension. The phenomenon is of course only observed under conditions in which (a) there is a sufficient degree of orientation, and (b) crystallization does not occur appreciably in the process of extension, that is, in a certain intermediate region between small and large extensions.

A precisely similar effect occurs also in vulcanized rubber, though in this case, owing to the presence of a more definite structural network, it is relatively less important, and is revealed only by a reduction or relaxation of the tension, at constant extension. Reference has already been made to this phenomenon in connexion with Wood and Roth's stress-temperature studies (Chap. II), and Goppel (1946 a) has directly observed an increase in crystallinity in vulcanized rubber accompanying the relaxation of stress. Unlike the relaxation or flow due to a breaking of cross-linkages or of molecular chains, this type of stress relaxation is reversible, and involves no permanent deformation. Both types of relaxation have been examined experimentally by Wildschut (1946), who finds the relaxation due to molecular orientation to reach a sharp maximum in the region of intermediate extensions. Field (1941) has also drawn attention to phenomena of a similar character.

## 2. Effect of crystallization on the stress-strain curve

The effect of crystallization on the shape of the stress-strain curve of a vulcanized rubber will depend on the precise manner in which the measurements are made. If the rubber is stretched to a given extension in such a way that the chains are brought into their equilibrium positions before crystallization begins (e.g. by raising the temperature), the process of crystallization will lead to a reduction in the tension. The stress-strain curve of the crystalline rubber will therefore fall below that of the amorphous material. If, on the other hand, crystallization takes place concurrently with the stretching, the effects are more complex. There is, firstly, the tendency to further crystalliza-tion, leading to a reduction in tension, and secondly, an increase in the effective number of junction points, which will tend to increase the tension. At high extensions, where the limiting extensibility of the network comes into play (Chap. VI), the second factor is likely to predominate. The maximum extensi-bility, which theoretically is proportional to the square root of the chain length, will become progressively diminished as the number of effective junction points is increased in the process of crystallization. (This will not happen if crystallization takes place only after the stretching is completed.)

Curves showing the reduction in extensibility with increasing crystallization are reproduced in Fig. 10.2. These curves were taken by the author from measurements carried out simul-taneously with the birefringence measurements represented in Fig. 9.11; the tension and birefringence data are therefore strictly comparable. The reduction of extensibility is not neces-sarily due solely to the crystallization factor; entanglements or other types of non-permanent junction points would also be expected to increase in number with reduction in temperature. That crystallization makes an important contribution to the observed changes is, however, clearly demonstrated by the anomalous position of the $-50°$ C. curve. The birefringence (Fig. 9.11) reveals less crystallization at this temperature than at the higher temperature of $-25°$ C.; correspondingly the extensibility is higher at the lower temperature.

In view of the rather serious modification of structure which crystallization introduces, and which is exemplified by these changes in the shape of the stress-strain curves, particularly in the region of very large extensions, it is obvious that the statis-tical theory of the amorphous network, in the form in which it is presented in Chapter VI, provides an insufficient quantitative basis for the discussion of such properties as the maximum extensibility of the network, at least in a material showing appreciable crystallization. Some writers have gone so far as to suggest that crystallization is the fundamental cause of

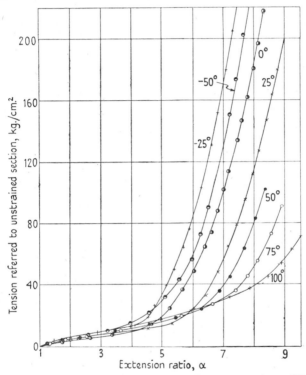

FIG. 10.2. Force-extension curves at various temperatures (°C.).

the upward curvature of the stress-strain curve. From the arguments put forward in Chapter VI, it would seem more appropriate to consider this curvature to be due primarily to the statistical properties of the amorphous network, but to be subject to modification in a quantitative sense by the additional complication of progressive crystallization.

## 3. Crystallization and tensile strength

In the last section it was shown that the ultimate tensile strength of raw rubber is largely determined by whether or not crystallization takes place during the extension, and there is reason to suppose that crystallization may similarly affect the tensile strength of a vulcanized rubber, though to a lesser extent, since there already exists a permanently cross-linked molecular network. Synthetic rubbers which do not crystallize, such as GR-S, generally give vulcanizates which are weak compared with those prepared from crystallizable rubbers, such as natural rubber or neoprene. Typical values of tensile strength for good quality natural rubber compounds without fillers ('pure-gum' compounds) are between 200 and 300 kg./cm.$^2$ (calculated on the unstrained cross-section), while comparable figures for GR-S are in the neighbourhood of only 30 kg./cm.$^2$ This difference may, however, be greatly reduced by the incorporation of a reinforcing carbon black. This has little effect on the tensile strength of the natural rubber, but brings the GR-S up to the same order of magnitude, e.g. 150–200 kg./cm.$^2$ The carbon particles are evidently capable of taking over the function performed by the crystallites in natural rubber.

*Flory's experiments on butyl rubbers*

In a highly interesting experimental investigation of the tensile strength of butyl rubbers, fractionated to give a range of molecular weights and subsequently vulcanized to the same degree of cross-linking, Flory (1946) obtained a close correlation between tensile strength and molecular weight before vulcanization. As will be seen from Fig. 10.3, which represents a typical series of fractions of different initial molecular weight $M$, the tensile strength is practically zero for fractions whose chain lengths are not sufficiently long to lead to the formation of a coherent cross-linked network during vulcanization. Beyond this point the tensile strength rises at first sharply, then more slowly with increasing molecular weight, finally becoming nearly independent of $M$ when this is sufficiently high. The tensile strength is therefore a function of molecular weight before vulcanization only over a relatively short range; when the initial chain length is very much greater than the segment length between junction points in the vulcanized rubber (which is constant for the series), the former ceases to have a significant effect. For the rubbers represented in Fig. 10.3 the 'chain molecular weight' in the vulcanized state was 37,000; the main increase of tensile strength occurred between $M$-values of 100,000 and 300,000.

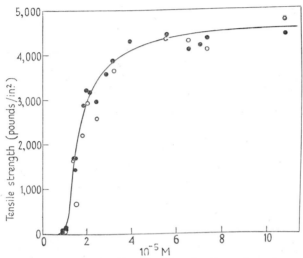

Fig. 10.3. Tensile strength of butyl rubber fractions of varying molecular weight ($M$) before vulcanization. (Flory, 1946.) ○ vulcanized 30 minutes. ● vulcanized 60 minutes.

In a semi-quantitative explanation of the shape of the curve of Fig. 10.3 advanced by Flory, the tensile strength is related to the fraction of the rubber which occurs in the form of principal network chains, that is, of chains which are linked to the network at two points at least. It is argued that it is only this fraction which is orientable and which is therefore suscep-tible to crystallization when the rubber is stretched; the remain-ing fraction (loose ends or completely unconnected molecules) contributes nothing to the stress, and acts more or less as a neutral diluent. This being so, the tensile strength might be expected to depend only on $w_a$, the proportion of active net-work chains in the material, which from Flory's theory of cross-linking (Chap. IV) is given by the expression

$$w_a = 1 - 2M_c/(M + M_c). \tag{10.1}$$

Plotting tensile strength against $1/(M+M_c)$ Flory finds, in fact, a linear relation, in accordance with this expectation (Fig. 10.4). The data for mixtures of fractions fall on the same straight line if the number-average molecular weight $M_n$ is substituted for $M$ in (10.1). There is, however, a quantitative discrepancy between the experimental results and the theo-

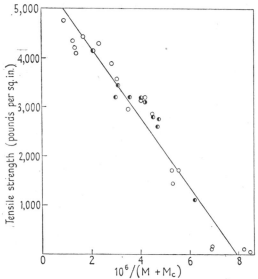

Fig. 10.4. Tensile strength of butyl rubbers plotted against $1/(M+M_c)$ for homogeneous fractions or $1/(M_n+M_c)$ for mixtures. ○ fractions. ◑ mixtures of fractions. ◑ unfractionated polymer. (Flory, 1946.)

retical prediction, for whereas according to equation (10.1) the tensile strength should vanish at $M = M_c$, i.e. in this particular case at $M = 37,000$, the experimental line cuts the zero axis at a point corresponding to $M = 89,000$. The tensile strength is therefore not directly proportional to the fraction of active chains, since at this value of $M$ the fraction of active chains (from 10.1) is not zero but 0·41. In other words, the tensile strength appears to vanish when there is still 41 per cent. of the polymer present in the form of a coherent network.

Flory considers the tensile strength in these butyl rubbers to be related directly to the degree of crystallinity, and explains the departure from direct proportionality between tensile strength and the proportion of active network chains on the basis that crystallization can only start in the presence of a certain minimum amount of orientable material.

### The effect of cross-linking on tensile strength

A similar hypothesis has been adopted by Gee (1947 a) to account for his experimental observations on natural rubber

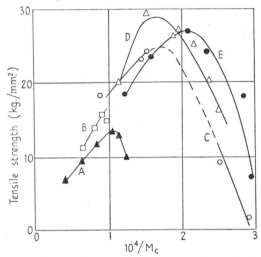

FIG. 10.5. Effect of cross-linking on tensile strength. A, Rubber-sulphur. B, T.M.T. compounds. C, Z.D.C. compounds. D, E, D.P.G.+M.B.T. with different proportions of sulphur. (Gee, 1947.)

vulcanizates. In these experiments the variation of tensile strength with degree of cross-linking or vulcanization was investigated, with the result shown in Fig. 10.5, in which tensile strength is plotted against the relative number of cross links, or reciprocal chain length $1/M_c$ estimated from modulus measurements. A number of types of compound, including both pure rubber-sulphur compounds, and compounds containing accelerators, were investigated. Except for the compound vulcanized with tetramethyl thiuram disulphide (T.M.T.), which covered an inadequate range, all the compounds showed the same type of variation, namely an increasing strength in the early stages of cross-linking, followed by a reduction to a low value as the degree of cross-linking was further increased. However, the

point at which the tensile strength was a maximum was found
to depend on the type of compound.

The effect of swelling the rubber in a hydrocarbon oil was to
shift the position of the maximum to lower degrees of cross-
linking, and at the same time to reduce its height (Fig. 10.6).
For a given amount of swelling the more highly cross-linked

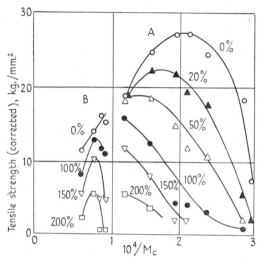

FIG. 10.6. Effect of swelling on tensile strength. $A$, D.P.G.+M.B.T.
compounds. $B$, T.M.T. compounds. Parameter, percentage solvent
added. (Gee, 1947.)

rubbers suffered a greater reduction of tensile strength than
those which were only lightly cross-linked.

According to the hypothesis put forward by Gee to explain
these effects, the tensile strength is a function of the degree
of crystallization existing in the compound at the extension
immediately preceding rupture. It is assumed further that the
degree of crystallization is determined approximately by the
amount of elongation (and is not directly dependent on degree
of cross-linking). If, in Fig. 10.7, the dotted curve represents
an assumed relation between the intrinsic breaking strength of
a rubber and the degree of elongation (which is related to
crystallization), the stress-strain curve for a highly cross-linked
rubber (i.e. high modulus, low extensibility) will intersect the

dotted curve at a point where crystallization has not yet started (curve 1); the tensile strength and elongation will therefore both be low. On the other hand, a lightly cross-linked rubber (curve 3) will intersect the dotted curve at a point corresponding to a high elongation, and therefore to a high degree of crystallization and a high tensile strength. This explains the increase in

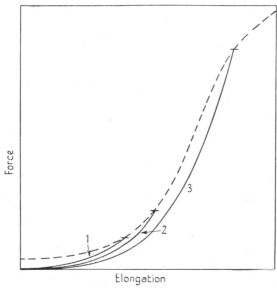

FIG. 10.7. Force-elongation curves for (1) high, (2) medium, and (3) low degrees of cross-linking (schematic). The dotted curve represents the hypothetical intrinsic strength.

tensile strength as the degree of cross-linking is reduced from a high value. There is, however, a limit to this process, for as in the case of the butyl rubbers discussed above, a certain degree of cross-linking is necessary to hold the structure together sufficiently for crystallization to start; if this minimum is not reached there will be plastic flow and correspondingly a very low strength, the strength ultimately falling to zero at a sufficiently low degree of cross-linking. By taking account of these two factors, reduction of flow and increase in modulus with increasing degree of cross-linking, Gee is thus able to account qualitatively for the observed relation between tensile strength and degree of vulcanization, and in particular for the appearance of a maximum at a certain moderate degree of vulcanization. It is consistent with this explanation that the more highly cross-linked rubbers break at relatively low elongations. In addition, the effect of a swelling agent is satisfactorily explained, for the imbibed liquid will shift the crystallization curve to

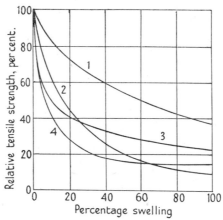

FIG. 10.8. Reduction in tensile strength on swelling. (Wildschut, 1946.)
(1) Natural rubber.   (2) Neoprene-G.   (3) Buna-S.   (4) Perbunan.

higher elongations (cf. Chap. VIII), thus displacing the maximum tensile strength in the direction of lower degrees of cross-linking and at the same time reducing its magnitude.

While crystallization may well play a dominant role in the determination of tensile strength in natural and butyl rubbers, it would be going too far to suggest that differences in the tensile behaviour of different rubber compounds are necessarily to be ascribed entirely, or even primarily, to this factor. Indeed, the observation that reinforcement by carbon black largely removes the wide difference between natural and GR-S rubbers shows that factors other than crystallization are probably of considerable importance. Also, a comparison of the diminution in tensile strength as a function of the degree of swelling by solvents for different rubbers reported by Wildschut (1946) shows natural rubber to retain its strength better than the non-crystallizing rubbers Buna-S (butadiene-styrene) and Perbunan (butadiene-acrylonitrile) (Fig. 10.8). Neoprene (poly-chloroprene), the other non-crystallizing rubber referred to, was about the same as Perbunan. These facts prove that a reduction in tensile strength on swelling is certainly not invariably caused by the suppression of crystallization, but may equally well result from a loosening of irregular intermolecular cohesions or entanglements.

## 4. Conclusion

The subject of breaking is a notoriously difficult one from the theoretical standpoint, and in rubbers particularly the complexity of the phenomena preclude any completely satisfactory theory at the present time. The foregoing discussion has been concerned with one aspect only of the phenomenon, namely the effect of crystallization, but a consideration of the wider question of the mechanism of breaking, particularly in amorphous rubbers, has not been attempted. W. Kuhn and H. Kuhn (1946 a) have actually put forward a theory of breaking, based on their statistical network model of non-Gaussian chains. In their treatment each chain is supposed to undergo an affine deformation, and it is further postulated that any particular chain will break when its extension exceeds the maximum hydrodynamic length by a small fractional amount. The chains thus break one by one as the tensile force is increased. At a certain point, however, the process becomes catastrophic; this is the theoretical breaking-point.

Without entering into a detailed discussion of W. Kuhn and H. Kuhn's theory, it should be pointed out that the assumption of an affine deformation of chains is not valid in the non-Gaussian region, and that a chain which is subjected to a particularly high tension, instead of breaking, may pull the associated junction points into new equilibrium positions.

Evidently there remains much to be done, both on the experimental and on the theoretical sides, before our understanding of the process of breaking in either amorphous or crystalline rubbers can be regarded as established on a sound basis.

# CHAPTER XI

# STRESS RELAXATION AND FLOW

## 1. General approach

In the discussion of the elasticity of rubber, particularly in Chapters IV to VIII, we have specifically limited ourselves to the purely elastic or equilibrium strain, and have endeavoured to eliminate subsidiary effects due to stress relaxation or other forms of non-ideal behaviour. In this and the succeeding chapter we shall consider this other aspect of the behaviour of rubber, including such phenomena as flow, internal viscosity, resilience, creep, and a variety of associated effects, all of which are, from the technological as well as from the scientific standpoint, of no less interest than the purely elastic properties. To these phenomena, in which both elastic and viscous effects are present simultaneously, the terms *visco-elastic* or *plastic-elastic* are frequently applied.

If a sample of unvulcanized rubber is subjected to a deformation for a specified time and then released, its subsequent retraction towards the original shape takes place in the manner illustrated in Fig. 11.1. After a lapse of several hours or days the rate of recovery becomes very slow, but if the temperature is raised, further recovery takes place, indicating the presence of internal elastic strain. Each successive increment of temperature leads to some further retraction. Even at 100° C. the elastic strain may not be completely removed, and in the example shown in Fig. 11.1 a further contraction was obtained by swelling the rubber with a suitable solvent, which was subsequently dried off. Clearly in a case like this both elastic and viscous processes are occurring at the same time, and any attempt to separate them quantitatively must necessarily be to a certain extent arbitrary and artificial.

This difficulty may be avoided in various ways. One method is to consider only the total deformation as a function of stress, time, etc., without attempting to separate it into recoverable (elastic) and non-recoverable (viscous) components. This method, which has been widely employed, for example, by Scott Blair (1945), has the advantage of being directly related to practical requirements. Another method is to consider a cyclic deformation, and to relate the energy loss in a cycle to the viscous component of the total deformation, whether or not there is flow in the sense of a permanent strain. This kind of

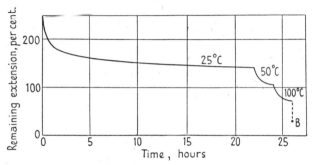

Fig. 11.1. Retraction of raw rubber after stretching to 390 per cent. extension. The point B was reached after swelling by solvent.

treatment, involving the conception of an internal viscosity, is useful in connexion with the behaviour of rubber in vibration. In a third method, applicable particularly to unvulcanized rubbers, elastic effects are eliminated by working under conditions of steady flow, arrived at, for example, by applying a constant rate of shear for a sufficiently long time. Under these conditions the stress, and therefore also the elastic component of the strain (however defined), ultimately become constant, and it is possible to measure a true flow, corresponding to the flow of an ordinary viscous fluid.

## 2. The measurement of flow in unvulcanized rubber

In this section we shall have to deal only with the third of the above methods—the measurement of flow in the ordinary sense.

No attempt will be made to review the many types of industrial *plastometers* designed with the object of measuring something more or less closely related to flow in this sense. Many of these are of limited scope, and are intended to give a measurement which shall bear a close relation to a particular industrial process, as, for example, the extrusion plastometer employed by Dillon and Johnston (1933). Those in more general use fall into two main classes. In the first class, represented by the *Williams plastometer*, a rubber cylinder is compressed between parallel plates under a constant load and the deformation measured as a function of time. This type of instrument does not eliminate elastic effects, though if the test is carried on for a sufficient time a state of steady flow may be approached. In a theoretical study Scott (1931) has shown that absolute measurements are possible with this instrument if the flow properties of the material conform to a certain law, but in general it is not possible to derive the flow curve from the experimentally obtained data. The second class of instrument, of which the *Mooney viscometer* is typical, makes use of the principle of continuous rotation, the stress being measured under a constant rate of shear. This type, besides being the most nearly ideal from the point of view of measuring true flow, has the advantage that it may be designed to give measurements of viscosity in absolute units.

Mooney has described two types of rotation viscometer. In the type (Mooney, 1936) designed for experimental investigations on the shape of the flow curve, i.e. the relationship between shear stress and rate of shear, the rubber is contained in the annular space between two coaxial cylinders. The outer fixed cylinder is divided longitudinally to facilitate filling, while a constant torque is applied to the inner movable cylinder by means of weights attached to a drum in the usual way. Both the inner and outer cylinders are maintained at constant temperature. The surfaces of the cylinders in contact with the rubber are deeply fluted to prevent slipping, and as a further precaution, pressure is maintained on the rubber by means of rings pressed against each of the open ends of the cylinder.

With this apparatus Mooney found that after an initial variation, usually lasting for only a fraction of a revolution, the rate of rotation became constant. From this constant rate of shear, and from the dimensions of the apparatus, it was then possible to calculate the absolute viscosity, as measured by the ratio of shear stress $S$ to rate of shear $d\sigma/dt$. Actually, rubbers show the phenomenon of non-Newtonian flow, i.e. the 'viscosity' is a function of the rate of shear. Their flow properties cannot therefore be represented by a single constant. This is illustrated in Fig. 11.2, which shows the relation between $\log(d\sigma/dt)$ and $\log S$, for a lightly milled crêpe rubber. Over a considerable

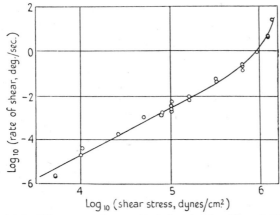

FIG. 11.2.   Flow curve for masticated natural rubber at 100° C.
Double logarithmic plot.   (Mooney, 1936.)

portion of the range the relation between these quantities was found to be linear. The flow curve could therefore be represented approximately by an equation of the Ostwald–de Waele type

$$d\sigma/dt = \psi S^n, \tag{11.1}$$

the value of $n$ in this particular case being 2·0. If the rate of shear was measured in radians per sec., and the stress in dynes per cm.², the value obtained for $\psi$ was $0\cdot9\times10^{-12}$, and the effective viscosity was $\eta = 1\cdot05\times10^6/S$ poises, this being defined as the ratio of shear stress to rate of strain for the particular value of stress under consideration.

The second type of machine described by Mooney (1934) was designed particularly for industrial use. The moving element (Fig. 11.3 (a)) in this machine is a circular disk, which is rotated at a constant speed in a stationary chamber. This chamber is made in two halves which can be separated across the plane

*AA'* for the purpose of filling; each half is in contact with a heavy platen maintained at constant temperature. The principles of operation are essentially the same as in the cylindrical instrument. The rubber is kept in close contact with the confining surfaces by means of a pressure applied through

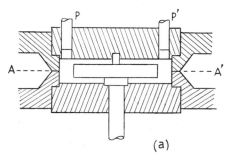

(a)

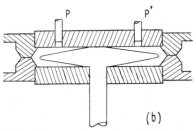

(b)

Fig. 11.3. The Mooney viscometer. (*a*) Original rotor. (*b*) Biconical rotor of Piper and Scott.

spring plungers *P*, *P'*, and in addition the surfaces are deeply cross-hatched. The normal speed of the disk is 2 revolutions per minute. The magnitude of the torque required to maintain this rate of rotation is derived from the thrust on the worm gear which drives the disk spindle; for details of the mechanism reference should be made to the original paper.

The 'shearing-disk' viscometer, while extremely valuable as an industrial instrument, does not give absolute values of viscosity in the case of a non-Newtonian fluid. The reason for this is that the rate of shear is not constant throughout the flowing mass, but varies in proportion to *r*, the distance of a point on the rotor from its axis of rotation. In addition there is a region round the edge of the disk where the state of flow can be only approximately represented. Mooney has given an analysis by which the 'mean viscosity' may be calculated in terms of the dimensional constants of the machine. This would be the true viscosity in the case of Newtonian flow. By carrying out a separate investigation of the shape of the flow curve for a particular rubber with the cylinder viscometer Mooney has shown that the mean viscosity thus derived agrees to within about 15 per cent. with that to be expected if the variation in effective viscosity with rate of shear from point to point is taken into account.

A more fundamental departure has been made by Piper and Scott (1945), who replaced the flat disk by a biconical rotor having a cross-section as shown in Fig. 11.3 (b), and modified the shape of the outer rim of the containing chamber. The effect of this is to make the rate of shear approximately independent of the radius, so that, at least to a first approximation, the rate of shear is the same throughout.

Difficulties arise in the neighbourhood of the edge, where the state of flow is not uniform; these were dealt with by introducing certain approximations. This modification therefore enables the absolute value of shear stress to be measured at a constant rate of flow, and hence, by varying the speed of rotation, it is possible to obtain the absolute flow curve. In this way Piper and Scott derived curves for both natural rubber (masticated) and GR-S which conformed with the Ostwald–de Waele relation (11.1), with values of the exponent $n$ of 2·0 and 3·1 respectively.

In a recent, more extensive study, using Piper and Scott's biconical rotor, Saunders and Treloar (1948) derived flow curves for masticated natural rubber at temperatures from 50° to 140° C. These are shown in Fig. 11.4, on a linear plot, and in Fig. 11.5 on a double logarithmic plot. The latter shows that the formula (11.1) does not adequately represent the form of the flow curves over an extensive range of rates of flow.

A very extensive series of investigations on the flow curves of both natural and synthetic rubbers has been carried out by

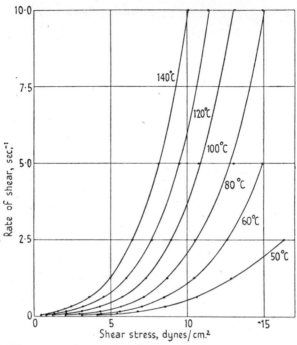

Fig. 11.4. Flow curves for masticated natural rubber at various temperatures. (Saunders and Treloar, 1948.)

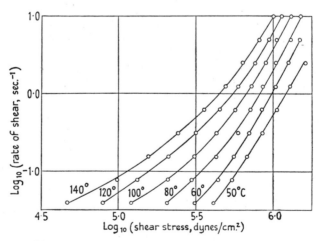

Fig. 11.5. Flow curves for masticated natural rubber, double logarithmic plot. (Saunders and Treloar, 1948.)

Hamm (1946), using a type of rotation viscometer very similar to Mooney's cylindrical form.

While his data were not accurately described by (11.1), most of his curves showed a considerable linear portion, from which values of $n$ could be derived.

For a plasticized rubber measured at different temperatures the value of this exponent was found to fall with increasing temperature from 3·3 at 30° C. to 1·85 at 90° C. The unplasticized rubber at a high temperature was comparable with the plasticized rubber at a lower temperature. Thus, both increase of temperature or plasticization (by milling) tended to reduce the extent of the departure from Newtonian flow ($n = 1$).

A selection from Hamm's data, including some for synthetic rubbers, is given in Table I.

TABLE I

*Values of $\psi$ and $n$ in equation $d\sigma/dt = \psi S^n$. (Hamm)*

Temperature of test, 70° C.

| Rubber | Treatment | $\psi$ | $n$ |
|---|---|---|---|
| Natural (crêpe) | Unmasticated | 0·0036 | 3·7 |
| ,, | Milled 1 hour 70° C. | 0·65 | 2·15 |
| Reclaimed rubber | — | 0·015 | 5·5 |
| Gutta-percha | — | 0·16 | 2·25 |
| Oppanol (polyisobutylene) | 4 hours 40° C. | 0·0022 | 1·5 |
| Buna-S (Butadiene-styrene) | ½ min. 40° C. | 3·6 | 4·1 |
| GR-S (Butadiene-styrene) | ¼ min. 50° C. | 0·83 | 4·05 |
| Stamikol (ethylene disulphide) | ¼ min. 40° C. | 0·012 | 1·2 |

## 3. The molecular basis of flow

*Eyring's theory*

There is no agreed basis for the theoretical discussion of flow processes in rubbers, or, for that matter, in ordinary liquids. This lack of a theoretical basis reflects the difficulties encountered in the development of a quantitative theory of the structure of liquids, about which less is known than is the case with either solids or gases.

It would not be appropriate in the present context to attempt a detailed discussion of theories of liquid structure. Of the theories of viscosity which have been proposed, that of Eyring has the advantage of having been extensively applied to the problem of flow in polymers, and will therefore be considered in some detail.

The basic ideas of liquid structure which are held to-day point to a close relation between the liquid and solid states. But whereas in a solid individual atoms can oscillate but cannot change their mean relative positions, in a liquid there is super-imposed on these atomic oscillations a degree of mobility of mean positions. Measurements of the self-diffusion of molten lead by Groh and von Hevesy (1920) have shown that an atom 'drifts' an average distance equal to the interatomic spacing in a time corresponding to 35 oscillations. From this conception two lines of developments are possible, as Mott and Gurney (1938) in a recent review article have shown. Either the atom may be supposed to move from one equilibrium position to another once in about 35 vibrations, or it may move a much smaller distance at each vibration. The first alternative forms the basis of Eyring's theory of viscosity, while the second is the starting-point of Andrade's theory.

In Eyring's theory the process of jumping from one equilibrium position to a new one may be thought of as taking place in the manner represented schematically in Fig. 11.6 (Hirschfelder, Stevenson, and Eyring, 1937). In switching over from the initial position to the new one, the moving atom or molecule has to pass through an intermediate state in which neighbouring molecules are to some extent pushed back; the intermediate state may therefore be represented as a state of higher energy, or a potential barrier, separating two potential minima. The effect of the shear stress is to reduce the effective height of this potential barrier to displacements in one direction while increasing its height with respect to displacements in the opposite direction. The effect of the stress is thus to render the number of thermally excited jumps taking place in either direction no longer equal, thus causing flow. The expression derived by

Eyring for the viscosity is (Glasstone, Laidler, and Eyring, 1941)

$$\eta = A \, \frac{M^{\frac{1}{2}} T^{\frac{3}{2}}}{V^{\frac{2}{3}} \Delta E_{\text{vap}}} \, e^{E_{\text{vis}}/RT}, \qquad (11.2)$$

where $A$ is a physical constant, $M$ and $V$ are the molecular weight and molar volume respectively, and $\Delta E_{\text{vap}}$ is the molar

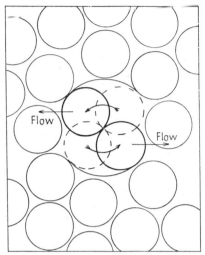

FIG. 11.6.  Schematic representation of flow process on Eyring's
theory. (Hirschfelder, Stevenson, and Eyring, 1937.)

heat of evaporation. The quantity $E_{\text{vis}}$ in the exponential factor measures the height of the potential barrier, and is called the 'energy of activation' for viscous flow.

### The energy of activation

On Eyring's theory the energy of activation for viscous flow would be expected to be related to the size of the molecule, which in turn is related to the heat of evaporation. For many low-molecular organic compounds it has been shown that the ratio of $E_{\text{vis}}$ to $\Delta E_{\text{vap}}$ is approximately equal to $\frac{1}{3}$ or $\frac{1}{4}$. For long-chain molecules, on the other hand, this ratio becomes progressively smaller with increasing chain length (Fig. 11.7). The value of $E_{\text{vis}}$ appears to approach a limit as the chain length increases. In the case of paraffins, this limit is about 6 to 7 k.cal. per mole. If we assume that the energy of activation is proportional to the length of the moving unit, we are forced to conclude from this observation that the moving unit is not necessarily the whole molecule but may be only a part of it. For the longest chains the length of the moving unit would appear to correspond to only about 25 carbon atoms along the chain.

It would perhaps be dangerous to accept this conclusion on the basis of a purely theoretical interpretation, were it not for

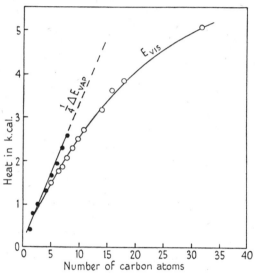

FIG. 11.7. Comparison of energy of activation for viscous flow and evaporation energy for paraffins. (Kauzmann and Eyring, 1940.)

the fact that it is entirely in harmony with our conception of the properties of long-chain molecules already developed. Only if the molecule were substantially rigid would it be expected to move as a whole. Since, however, we have very good reasons for thinking of the molecule as flexible, like a chain with more or less freely jointed links, we should expect *a priori* that the correlation between the movements of two points $A$ and $B$ on a molecule would diminish rather rapidly as the distance $AB$ (measured along the chain) is increased. Eyring's conclusion suggests that the average length of chain capable of coordinated movement in viscous flow is about 25 carbon atoms. Comparable figures have been obtained for the energy of activation for viscous flow in natural rubber. Using the data represented in Fig. 11.5, Saunders and Treloar (1948) plotted the logarithm of the rate of flow, at a given stress, against the reciprocal of the absolute temperature, and obtained the set of linear relations shown in Fig. 11.8. The slope of these lines showed a

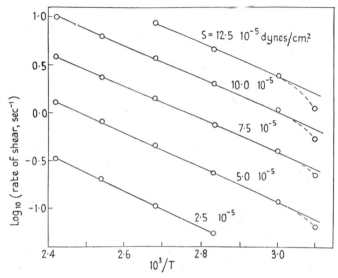

FIG. 11.8. Log($d\sigma/dt$) plotted against $1/T$, for various values of shear stress. (Saunders and Treloar, 1948.)

small, but hardly significant dependence on stress, yielding an average value of 8·1 k.cal./mole for the energy of activation involved in the flow process. An earlier study by Smallwood (1937), employing the data obtained by Mooney from his cylindrical plastometer, led to a figure of 10·2 k.cal./mole. These figures are of the same order of magnitude as the figure quoted above for paraffin molecules.

### Dependence of viscosity on chain length

The activation energy is not the only factor determining viscosity, and the fact that this quantity may ultimately become independent of chain length does not imply that the viscosity is similarly independent. For in addition to the rate of jumping of the individual units of flow it is necessary to take into account the degree of coordination between these individual processes. No satisfactory theoretical method of attacking this problem appears to have been found. Experimentally, however, the form of the relation between chain length and viscosity has been determined by Flory (1940), who made a very complete study of a series of polyesters of molecular weights ranging from 200 to 10,000. The viscosities of these materials (which did not exhibit appreciable departure from Newtonian flow) were shown by Flory to be described with remarkable accuracy by the formula

$$\ln \eta = A + B/T + CM_w^{\frac{1}{2}}, \qquad (11.3)$$

where $M_w$ is the weight-average molecular weight. The constant $B$, which is related to the activation energy, yielded values of this quantity in the neighbourhood of 8 k.cal./mole (varying with molecular constitution). This corresponds to a unit of flow of about 30 chain atoms.

## 4. Stress relaxation

The methods of measuring flow discussed above relate only to the final steady state, in which the elastic component of the deformation is not changing. In this section the more complex phenomena occurring in the initial period, when both elastic and viscous processes are present, will be considered. Measurements of these visco-elastic phenomena are conveniently divided into two classes. First, there is the type of experiment in which the strain is held constant, while the variation of stress as a function of time is studied. Secondly, there is the type of experiment in which the stress is held constant, while the variation of strain with time is investigated. In this class may be included also experiments performed under conditions in which the applied force, rather than the stress, is held constant. The first class may be called stress-relaxation experiments, while the effects studied under the second class are usually referred to as flow or creep phenomena. It is perhaps better to use the term 'creep' (even though the rate of strain may not be small) in this connexion, so that the word 'flow' may be reserved for the purely irreversible type of deformation.

Considerable insight into the nature of the stress-relaxation processes in vulcanized rubber has been gained from the work of Tobolsky and co-workers. Fig. 11.9 shows some of the experimental data of Tobolsky and Andrews (1945) for a vulcanized natural rubber, without fillers, at four different temperatures.

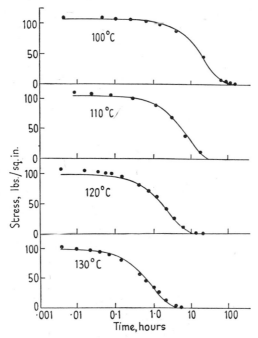

Fig. 11.9. Stress relaxation in vulcanized rubber at various temperatures; 50 per cent. elongation. (Tobolsky and Andrews, 1945.) ● ● experimental. ▬ theoretical.

The ordinates represent the stress and the abscissae time (plotted on a logarithmic scale). It was found that each set of data could be represented by an exponential decay formula of the type

$$f = f_0 e^{-k't}, \tag{11.4}$$

in which the value of the constant $k'$ is a function of the temperature. The dependence of $k'$ on temperature was found to fit the Eyring formula for a unimolecular reaction rate, i.e.

$$k' = (kT/h)e^{-\Delta H/RT}, \tag{11.5}$$

where $\Delta H$ is the heat of activation and $h$ is Planck's constant.

The degree of agreement between these experimental data and the theoretical relations (11.4) and (11.5) is well shown in Fig. 11.9.

This type of relaxation of stress was shown by Tobolsky and Andrews to be due to a breaking of the chain molecules by an

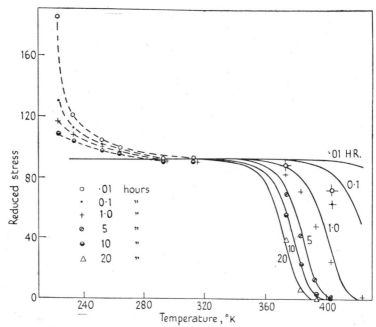

Fig. 11.10. Stress as function of temperature after various times.
(Tobolsky and Andrews, 1945.)

oxidative reaction. Exclusion of air, or incorporation of an anti-oxidant in the rubber mixture, led to a reduction in the rate of relaxation, in the former case by a factor of 1,000.

In general, the synthetic rubbers examined did not fit the formula (11.4), but were more spread out on the time scale, suggesting that more than one chemical reaction was involved.

This high-temperature relaxation, involving chemical breakdown, was not, however, the only type encountered. At low temperatures another type of relaxation was found to be far more important. This is illustrated in Fig. 11.10, which represents the variation of stress with temperature at various times after the beginning of the extension. It is apparent from this figure that there are three rather clearly defined regions. In the first region, corresponding to low temperatures and short times, a type of relaxation associated with secondary cohesions due to van der Waals' forces between the chains predominates, while at the other extremity, corresponding to high temperatures and long times, the relaxation is due to oxidative degradation. Between these two regions there is a considerable range of temperature and time in which there is very little stress relaxation. This, which corresponds roughly with the region in which rubber is normally employed, represents a state in which the molecular network reaches its equilibrium configuration under the applied stress.

Unlike the primary bond breakage, the secondary bond breakage phenomenon revealed at low temperatures could not be represented by equation (11.4), that is, by a single time of relaxation.

## 5. Creep

In some rubbers there is a very close relation between the high-temperature stress relaxation and creep. In the treatment adopted by Tobolsky and Andrews the stress $f$ at the instant $t$ is used to define the number of chains $N$ which remain unbroken up till that time, according to the relation

$$f = NkT(\alpha - 1/\alpha^2), \tag{11.6}$$

$\alpha$ being the extension ratio, and $NkT$ the 'modulus'. By this means the variation of $N$ with time, either in creep or in stress relaxation, may be determined. The result of such an investigation, using natural rubber, is shown in Fig. 11.11. The correlation between the creep and stress-relaxation data for this material is seen to be very close. It is interesting also to find that the rate of structural breakdown is independent of the amount of the extension. Similar results were obtained with butyl rubber, but in the case of GR-S the creep curve lay somewhat higher than the stress-relaxation curve. Other experiments, in which the change of modulus under intermittent loading was compared with that under continuous loading, showed that this discrepancy was due to the re-formation of cross-linkages as a result of chemical reactions taking place concurrently with the degradation reaction. The general relation between stress relaxation and creep when both chain-breaking (scission) and cross-linking reactions are present is rather complex, and has been dealt with in a later paper by

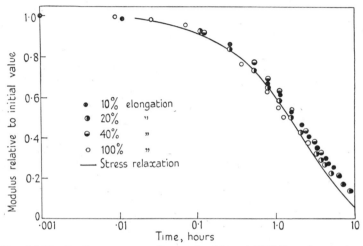

FIG. 11.11. Continuous creep of natural rubber at 120° C. under constant load. (Tobolsky and Andrews, 1945.)

Green and Tobolsky (1946). Their method is based on the assumption that the network elements formed by cross-linkage in the course of a stress-relaxation or creep experiment are initially in their most probable configurations, i.e. unstressed. Hence, in a continuous relaxation experiment the modulus at any instant is simply proportional to the number of chains remaining unbroken, since the newly cross-linked chains contribute nothing to the stress. But if the same rubber is maintained in the unstressed condition (except while measuring the modulus), the reduction in the modulus is proportional to the difference between the number of cross-links broken and the number re-formed. Comparison of continuous and intermittent stress-relaxation curves thus provides direct evidence on the relative rates of the chain scission and cross-linking reactions.

In a creep experiment conditions are more complicated. Though each chain element formed by cross-linkage is initially in the relaxed state, it will not immediately contribute to the modulus. But as the strain increases it will become increasingly extended, and will therefore contribute more and more to the modulus. The effective modulus at any time will thus depend not only on the number of chains broken, but also on the number of chains re-formed, and *on the precise time at which they are re-formed*.

## 6. The principle of superposition

The existence of phenomena such as stress relaxation and non-linear creep implies that the behaviour of the material is determined not only by the applied stress at the time considered, but also by its previous stress history. By a principle enunciated by Boltzmann in 1874 it is possible to predict the behaviour when the applied stress varies with time in any arbitrary manner if the behaviour under constant stress is known. This principle states that the total deformation produced at any time due to a complex loading history is the sum of the deformations which would be produced by each of the separate loads, removal of a load being regarded as the application of a negative load (Leadermann, 1943). It is fundamental to the proof of this principle of superposition that the deformations (both instantaneous and time-dependent) shall be proportional to the stresses, hence it can in any case only be applied when the strains are small. It has been shown to apply accurately to glass, but the limitation to small strains detracts from its quantitative application to rubbers. Leadermann (1943) has tested its applicability to polyvinyl chloride and found it to account well for the observed delayed elastic effects, provided that the strains were small ($< 10$ per cent.). In particular, the variation of length with time when the stress was applied intermittently could be predicted from the result of a continuous-loading experiment. For strains greater than about 10 per cent. however, the agreement was less exact.

Kohlrausch demonstrated qualitatively a rather striking

consequence of Boltzmann's superposition principle in 1876. He noticed that the subsequent retraction of a piece of strained rubber takes place more slowly the longer the time for which it is held in the strained state. Hence if it is strained first in one direction for a long time, then in the opposite direction for a short time, the effects of the first straining will persist after the effects of the second straining have disappeared. Consequently, it is possible to obtain a reversal of the direction of retraction. This reversal was actually observed. Indeed, by a suitable arrangement of initial deformations Kohlrausch obtained two reversals of the direction of retraction.

We may anticipate the analytical methods discussed in the next chapter by referring here to the possibility of representing the behaviour of a material in terms of a number of cohesive mechanisms each having its own time of relaxation. The use of such a model implies that the stresses obey the superposition principle, and it may be shown that a system described by $n$ relaxation times can be made to give $n-1$ reversals of the type described by Kohlrausch. Furthermore, as Leadermann (1943) points out, if we can find a distribution of relaxation times which reproduces the behaviour of a material under any given strain history, its behaviour under any other conditions of straining may be referred to the same model.

# CHAPTER XII

# DYNAMIC PROPERTIES OF RUBBERS

## 1. Resilience

AMONG the practically important properties of a rubber, resilience, or the capacity for storing and returning energy in a rapid deformation, is necessarily given a high place. A rubber which shows good elastic properties under a slow deformation does not necessarily have good resilience. This is strikingly demonstrated by comparing a ball made of natural rubber with one of butyl rubber; to the feel both have apparently a similar degree of elasticity. But when dropped the first ball bounces nearly to the height from which it was released, whilst the second barely leaves the ground. However, if the experiment is repeated at a high temperature, say 100° C., the butyl ball will be found to bounce almost as well as the other.

This experiment shows the importance of the two parameters, time and temperature, in determining the elastic response of a rubber-like material.

A number of investigations into the effect of temperature on resilience have been reported in the literature. Among these, it will be sufficient for the present purpose to quote the recent work of Mullins (1947), who measured the rebound of a pendulum bob after impact with a rubber block. Examples of the data obtained are shown in Fig. 12.1, in which the resilience, defined as the ratio of energy after to energy before impact, is plotted against temperature, for several types of rubber. It will be seen that in all cases the resilience passes through a minimum, which, except in the case of butyl rubber, is rather sharply defined. The temperature of minimum resilience is closely correlated with the second-order transition temperature (Chap. I) at which the rubber loses its long-range elasticity, as the following table shows. Except for butyl rubber, which is slightly anomalous, the second-order transition occurs at between 15° and 20° C. below the minimum resilience temperature. Furthermore, the incorporation of a plasticizer lowers the temperature of minimum resilience (Mullins, 1947), just as it lowers the temperature of the second-order transition. Addition of carbon black broadens the resilience-temperature curve, without, however, affecting the position of the minimum. These

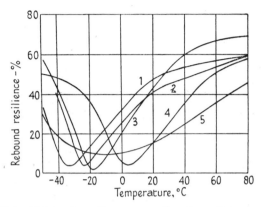

Fig. 12.1. Rebound resilience as a function of temperature. (Mullins, 1947.) (1) Natural rubber. (2) GR-S (butadiene-styrene). (3) Neoprene (polychloroprene). (4) Hycar OR-15 (butadiene-acrylonitrile). (5) Butyl rubber.

TABLE I

*Comparison of temperature of minimum resilience with second-order transition temperature*

| Rubber (vulcanized) | Minimum resilience (Mullins) | Second-order transition (from 'Rubber in Engineering', p. 202) |
| --- | --- | --- |
| Natural . . . | −35° C. | −55° C. |
| GR-S . . . . | −25° C. | −45° C. |
| Neoprene GN . . | −19° C. | −35° C. |
| Butyl . . . . | −10° C. | −50° C. |
| Hycar OR-15 . . | 5° C. | −10° C. |

observations suggest that the resilience is intimately associated with the structure of the molecule and the nature of the inter-molecular forces, and not with the gross structure of the material. This is further exemplified by the effect obtained by Mullins with a vulcanizate containing an intimate mixture of two different rubbers—natural rubber and Hycar OR-15—which, as shown in Fig. 12.2, yielded a resilience-temperature curve containing a double minimum, as if the two components of the mixture were effectively separated. This is to be contrasted with the behaviour of a co-polymer, such as GR-S (Fig. 12.1) which shows only a single sharp minimum.

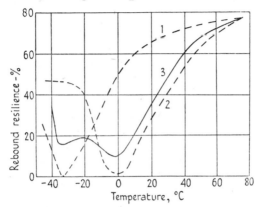

FIG. 12.2. Effect on resilience of compounding two rubbers together. (Mullins, 1947.) (1) Natural rubber. (2) Hycar OR-15. (3) 50-50 mixture.

## 2. General analysis of relaxation phenomena

### The Maxwell model

A number of aspects of the phenomena of resilience and dynamic properties of rubber generally may be correlated in terms of a purely formal scheme involving the conception of relaxation or orientation times. This scheme, which rests on bases originally formulated by Boltzmann, Kelvin, and Maxwell, has been widely invoked for the representation of the behaviour of materials of all kinds which do not fit into the simple classification into elastic solids or Newtonian (viscous) liquids.

Maxwell considered viscosity from the standpoint of a continuous breakdown of the elastic reaction to the applied stress, which is continually being renewed. The strain at any time $t$ was regarded as made up of two components, of which one, the elastic component, was assumed to be proportional to the applied stress, while the other, the viscous component, was assumed to be such that the *rate of increase* of strain was proportional to the stress (as in Newtonian flow). The differential

equation connecting stress $S$, strain $\sigma$, and time $t$ then takes
the form

$$\frac{d\sigma}{dt} = \frac{1}{G}\frac{dS}{dt} + \frac{S}{\eta},\qquad(12.1)$$

where $G$ and $\eta$ are constants corresponding respectively to a
modulus of elasticity and a viscosity. In the case when the

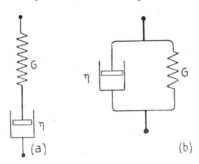

FIG. 12.3. Models representing (a) Maxwell
liquid and (b) Kelvin solid.

strain is held constant, $d\sigma/dt = 0$, and equation (12.1) leads to
the exponential decay of stress with time

$$S = S_0 e^{-Gt/\eta} = S_0 e^{-t/\tau},\qquad(12.2)$$

the constant $\tau$, which is equal to $G/\eta$, being termed the *time
of relaxation*.

From the mathematical point of view equation (12.2) represents the simplest possible expression which can be used to
represent a stress decay, and it is because of this simplicity,
combined with the fact that a large number of physical systems
have been found to behave approximately according to this
law, that Maxwell's concept has been so frequently applied.
The concept is not limited to shear strain, but is equally
applicable to any system governed by an elastic and resistive
coefficient. In the case of elongation or compression the appropriate constants would be Young's modulus and the 'coefficient
of viscous traction'.

In the case when the stress is held constant we have, from
(12.1), $d\sigma/dt = S/\eta$, i.e. a rate of flow depending only on the
viscous term.

It is possible to represent a system of the type governed by equation (12.1) by means of a mechanical model consisting of a spring in series with a dashpot (Fig. 12.3 (a)). If this model is suddenly extended, the spring will extend until it is in equilibrium with the applied force. If the deformation is then held constant, the spring will relax exponentially as the dashpot slowly responds to the stress.

### The Kelvin model

The Maxwell model may be regarded as representing in a simple way the properties of a liquid which possesses elasticity. For times which are short compared with the relaxation time the elastic effects predominate, while for times large compared with the relaxation time the viscous effects are most apparent.

An alternative model, suggested by Kelvin, and independently by Voigt, consisting of a spring and dashpot in parallel (Fig. 12.3 (b)), may be regarded as the prototype of the viscous solid. It is defined by the differential equation

$$S = \eta \frac{d\sigma}{dt} + G\sigma. \tag{12.3}$$

It is not possible to apply an instantaneous deformation to this model. If, however, a constant stress is applied, the strain increases according to the law

$$\sigma = \frac{S}{G}(1 - e^{-Gt/\eta}) = \frac{S}{G}(1 - e^{-t/\tau'}), \tag{12.4}$$

reaching the value corresponding to the equilibrium extension of the spring as $t$ becomes indefinitely large. On removal of the stress, there is no immediate elastic retraction, but the strain decreases exponentially to zero. The constant $\tau'$ in the exponential term is usually called a *retardation time* (Burgers, 1939), or alternatively, an *orientation time* (Tuckett, 1942).

In the Maxwell model the same stress is applied to each component, and the total strain is the sum of the strains in each component. In the Kelvin model, on the other hand, the strains in each component are the same, and the stresses are additive.

In making use of these models, or of others of a similar but more complicated character, it is important always to remember that they are of a purely empirical nature. It cannot be assumed that the possibility of describing the behaviour of a system in terms of a particular model necessitates or implies the physical existence of elements in the actual system (e.g. of a molecular character) in any way corresponding to the components of the model, though such a correspondence is of course not precluded. The model may be useful in suggesting possible physical mechanisms, but the validity of such suggestions must be established by independent evidence. Used with caution, and with a proper respect for their limitations, mechanical models of the kind envisaged may be valuable subsidiary aids to the description and interpretation of complex types of visco-elastic behaviour.

## 3. Application to real materials

The behaviour of rubbers in general does not correspond exactly to either the Maxwell or Kelvin models, and it is necessary to make use of multiple-element systems. Thus, in one of his earlier papers Kuhn (1939) considered the general case in which the stress at constant strain was representable as the sum of a number of separately relaxing Maxwell terms, thus

$$S = S_{10}e^{-t/\tau_1} + S_{20}e^{-t/\tau_2} + \ldots = \sum_i S_{i0}e^{-t/\tau_i}, \qquad (12.5)$$

each characterized by a distinctive relaxation time $\tau_i$, the whole system corresponding to the arrangement represented in Fig. 12.11. Furthermore, he calculated the mean relaxation time $\bar{\tau}$ for simple liquids, using the relation $\bar{\tau} = G/\eta$ and assuming the elastic modulus to have a value not very different from that for the solid. In this way, the mean relaxation time for water at 20° C. was found to be of the order $0.3 \times 10^{-12}$ sec. This is, of course, sufficiently rapid to be beyond the range of ordinary measurements. Glasses, on the other hand, may be regarded as liquids possessing a very large relaxation time; as the temperature is raised the relaxation time decreases. The temperature at which the glass transforms to a liquid in the ordinary sense corresponds to a relaxation time of the order of about a minute, and the corresponding viscosity is in the region $10^{11}$ to $10^{13}$ poises. Kuhn regarded a rubber as a system characterized by two relaxation times, one very short, as in a liquid, and one infinitely large. The first was attributed to local intermolecular cohesions, and was associated with an elastic modulus of the order $10^{11}$ dynes/cm.$^2$, while the second was attributed to the entropy elasticity of the molecular network, with a modulus of about $10^7$ dynes/cm.$^2$ More recently Kuhn and Künzle (1947) have examined the question of the relaxation times in more detail and put forward a more comprehensive scheme; however, this simple model is often helpful. The second-order transition temperature in a rubber, as Tuckett (1942) has pointed out, may be regarded as the temperature at which the mean relaxation time becomes comparable with the time of observation (e.g. 1 minute) and corresponds with the 'unfreezing' of the secondary forces between molecules, but whereas in a liquid this unfreezing results in viscous flow, in rubbers it is revealed in the highly elastic deformation. Thus the transition temperature is correlated not with the overall viscosity but with the internal viscosity accompanying the process of extension of the molecular chains.

Qualitatively, Kuhn's simple model, in which only a single (mean) relaxation-time is considered, affords an explanation of the resilience phenomena discussed above, and illustrated in Fig. 12.1. At high temperatures the relaxation time is short, and the stress at any instant corresponds very nearly with the equilibrium elastic deformation of the network. Under these conditions the force-deformation curve is nearly reversible. The loss is therefore small and the resilience high. At the other extreme, at sufficiently low temperatures, the time of relaxation is very large compared with the time of impact (0·01 sec.), and again there is little loss. In this region, however, the resilience corresponds to a different type of elasticity, an elasticity comparable with that of an ordinary hard solid, rather than with that of a rubber in the usual sense. In the intermediate region, where the time of relaxation is comparable with the time of impact, the network deformation is partial and lags behind the applied stress. This hysteresis leads to energy loss and low resilience.

## 4. Cyclic deformations—Aleksandrov and Lazurkin

A more controllable method of studying the dependence of the relaxation processes on time and temperature is by means of cyclic deformations at various frequencies. The deforming force may be applied either mechanically or electromagnetically. Using the former method, Aleksandrov and Lazurkin (1939) carried out an extensive investigation which brings out very clearly the essential basis of the phenomena shown by rubbers under alternating stress.

The rubber to be examined was in the form of a short cylinder which could be compressed between two parallel plates, of which the lower one was fixed while the upper was attached to a steel spring. The other end of this spring was subjected to an oscillatory displacement. Since the maximum compression of the rubber was small compared with the compression of the spring, this system gave a variation of applied force which was approximately sinusoidal, and whose amplitude was substantially independent of the deformation of the rubber. The amplitude of the deformation of the rubber was measured by an optical device. The natural frequency of the spring assembly was well above the highest frequencies employed; resonance effects were therefore avoided.

Fig. 12.4 shows in a concise form the variation of amplitude of deformation with frequency and with temperature. At a given frequency the deformation is very small below a temperature corresponding to the transformation point. As the temperature is raised the deformation increases, over a range of about 40° C., after which it approaches constancy. An increase of frequency displaces the curve, without greatly altering its shape. For natural rubber an increase of frequency by a factor of 10 is equivalent in its effect on mechanical properties to a reduction of temperature of about 8° C.

To interpret these results, Aleksandrov and Lazurkin consider the total deformation $\sigma$ to be divisible into two parts of which the first part $\sigma_{OE}$ takes place substantially instantaneously, while the second part $\sigma_{HE}$ is governed by a retardation time $\tau'$ of the type which characterizes a Kelvin solid. The total deformation may then be expressed as a function of the time, thus

$$\sigma = \sigma_{OE} + \sigma_{HE} = \sigma_{OE} + \sigma_{HE\infty}(1 - e^{-t/\tau'}).\qquad(12.6)$$

From the structural standpoint the first term corresponds to the separation of atoms, without change of molecular configuration. This is the 'ordinary elasticity' of a glassy or crystalline solid,

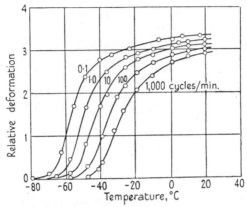

Fig. 12.4. Relation between amplitude of vibration and temperature at various frequencies. (Aleksandrov and Lazurkin, 1939.)

governed by a Young's modulus of the order $10^{11}$ dynes/cm.$^2$ The second term represents the true 'high elasticity' of the rubber, associated with the configurational entropy of the network. The time constant $\tau'$ is related to the time required for the molecules to change their configurations. If the time $t$ is sufficiently long, the highly elastic deformation reaches its equilibrium value $\sigma_{HE\infty}$, corresponding to a modulus of the order $10^7$ dynes/cm.$^2$

To bring in the effect of temperature, Aleksandrov and Lazurkin make the assumption that the time of orientation (like viscous flow) is governed by the rate of passage of chain segments across potential barriers, and write

$$\tau' = Ae^{E/kT}.\qquad(12.7)$$

Substituting this relation in equation (12.6), they then obtain an expression representing the dependence of strain on both

time and temperature. A typical set of curves obtained from
this equation is shown in Fig. 12.5.

In the case of an alternating stress of frequency $\omega/2\pi$ the
dependence of amplitude of deformation on the frequency may

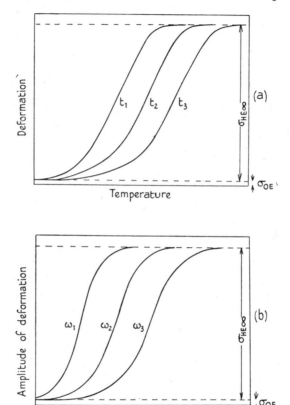

FIG. 12.5. Deformation under (a) steady stress, and (b) oscillating
stress of frequency $\omega$. (Aleksandrov and Lazurkin, 1939.)

readily be derived. For convenience we may depart from
Aleksandrov and Lazurkin's exposition by omitting the relatively unimportant term $\sigma_{OE}$. This leaves the simple Kelvin
model, as represented in Fig. 12.3 (b), having the differential
equation (12.3). For a sinusoidal stress given by

$$S = S_0 \cos \omega t \qquad (12.8)$$

equation (12.3) has the steady-state solution

$$\sigma = \sigma_0 \cos(\omega t - \delta) \qquad (12.9)$$

representing a deformation of the same frequency, but differing in phase from the applied stress. Writing $\eta/G = \tau'$, the amplitude $\sigma_0$ is given by

$$\sigma_0 = \frac{S_0}{G}(1 + \omega^2 \tau'^2)^{-\frac{1}{2}}. \qquad (12.9\,a)$$

If the temperature-dependence of $\tau'$ is given by (12.7), the curves expressing the relation between amplitude and tempera-

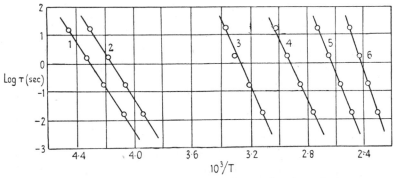

Fig. 12.6. Relation between log (retardation time) and reciprocal temperature. (Aleksandrov and Lazurkin, 1939.) (1) Vulcanized natural rubber. (2) Polychloroprene. (3) Semi-ebonite. (4) Polymethyl methacrylate with 30 per cent. plasticizer. (5) Polymethyl methacrylate with 10 per cent. plasticizer. (6) Polymethyl methacrylate without plasticizer.

ture, for different frequencies, then have the form shown in Fig. 12.5 (b). These curves give a very fair representation of the experimental behaviour.

From their experimental curves, Aleksandrov and Lazurkin were able to calculate the retardation time $\tau'$ as a function of temperature. Their results for a number of rubbers, shown in Fig. 12.6, yielded in all cases a linear dependence of $\log \tau'$ on $1/T$, thus substantiating equation (12.7). The temperature range was perhaps rather small for the accurate evaluation of the activation energy $E$; approximately however, the activation energy for natural rubber and neoprene calculated from their data is 39 k.cal./mole. This is of a higher order of magnitude than the energy of activation for viscous flow, which, as we have seen, is about 8 k.cal./mole.

It should be noted that the above analysis is based on a model in which the spring element is linear. This assumption was sufficiently near the truth for the deformations employed in Aleksandrov and Lazurkin's experiments, which amounted only to a few per cent. of the undeformed dimensions of the specimen.

## 5. Resonance phenomena

*Theory*

In the preceding section inertia effects in the moving system

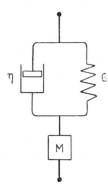

FIG. 12.7. Model used for analysis of vibration phenomena.

were not considered. If, however, the frequency is sufficiently high, or the mass of the moving element sufficiently large, such effects can become of supreme importance. The system which is generally used as a basis for analysis under these conditions is equivalent to a Kelvin element in series with a mass $M$ (Fig. 12.7). The differential equation governing the motion of this system under the action of an oscillatory stress is

$$M\frac{d^2\sigma}{dt^2} + \eta\frac{d\sigma}{dt} + G\sigma = S_0\cos\omega t, \quad (12.10)$$

and the steady-state solution has the form

$$\sigma = \frac{S_0\cos(\omega t - \delta)}{[(G - M\omega^2)^2 + \omega^2\eta^2]^{\frac{1}{2}}}, \quad (12.11)$$

where

$$\tan\delta = \eta\omega/(G - M\omega^2). \quad (12.11a)$$

If the frequency is varied the amplitude passes through a maximum, corresponding to the condition of resonance. The resonant frequency $\omega_0$ is obtained by differentiating the first factor in (12.11) with respect to $\omega$, and is given by

$$G = M\omega_0^2 + \eta^2/2M. \quad (12.12a)$$

On the other hand, if the mass is treated as the independent variable the condition for resonance becomes

$$G = M\omega_0^2. \quad (12.12b)$$

In practice the two expressions (12.12 *a*) and (12.12 *b*) are normally indistinguishable, since $\eta^2/2M$ is generally small compared with $M\omega_0^2$. At low temperatures, however, it might become a matter of importance to distinguish between resonance under conditions of variable frequency and variable mass, respectively.

### Experimental studies

In the numerous studies of the so-called dynamic modulus and dynamic viscosity of rubbers, based on the application of

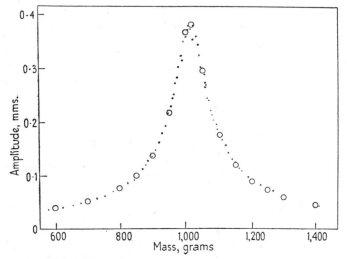

FIG. 12.8. Resonance curve for pure gum rubber. (Gehman, Woodford, and Stambaugh, 1941.) o o o Theoretical. · · · Observed.

the above equations, the usual method has been to apply an oscillating stress of determinable magnitude electromagnetically. For this purpose it is convenient to attach the moving element to a coil carrying alternating current mounted in the field of an electromagnet. Means are provided for varying either the frequency of the alternating current or the mass attached to the moving system, and for determining the amplitude of vibration.

Working with a pure gum rubber in compression, and varying the mass, Gehman, Woodford, and Stambaugh (1941) obtained in this way the resonance curve shown in Fig. 12.8, which agrees very closely with the theoretical form given by (12.11). Mixtures containing carbon black, however, yielded curves of an unsymmetrical shape, which did not agree at all well with the

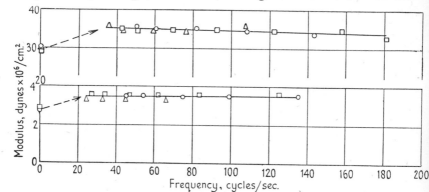

FIG. 12.9. Dynamic modulus as a function of frequency. (Dillon, Prettyman, and Hall, 1944.) *Bottom*, pure rubber compound. *Top*, rubber-carbon black (30 per cent.) compound.

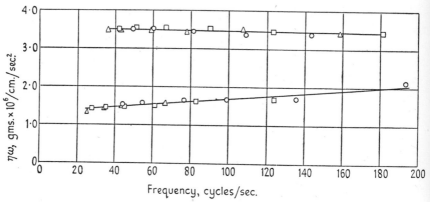

FIG. 12.10. The product $\eta\omega$ as a function of frequency. (Dillon, Prettyman, and Hall, 1944.) *Bottom*, pure rubber compound. *Top*, rubber-carbon black (30 per cent.) compound.

theory. This departure was attributed to a variation of the constants $G$ and $\eta$ with amplitude of vibration. The cause of this variation, which has been postulated also by other workers, has not been established.

The general nature of the dependence of the elastic and viscous coefficients on frequency is illustrated in Figs. 12.9 and

12.10, taken from the work of Dillon, Prettyman, and Hall (1944). These data, which refer to shear vibrations, agree with those of other workers in showing only a small dependence of dynamic modulus on frequency. The dynamic viscosity, on the other hand, shows a strong frequency dependence; in fact the product $\eta\omega$ is roughly constant. This inverse relationship between frequency and dynamic viscosity has also been frequently observed.

This conclusion, that the dynamic viscosity is a function of frequency, reveals the inadequacy of the model (Fig. 12.7) and of the associated differential equation (12.10) on which the original analysis of the vibration problem was based. If, as it appears, the constants in this equation are functions of frequency, the behaviour is clearly more complicated than we had originally supposed. In particular, it follows that the properties cannot be represented in terms of a single retardation time. We shall see below that, by choosing a suitable distribution of retardation or relaxation times, it is possible to account for the observed type of dependence of dynamic viscosity on frequency.

## 6. The distribution of relaxation times

It has long been recognized that the representation of complex types of visco-elastic behaviour requires the introduction of a multiplicity of relaxation times. Fig. 12.11 represents a system of Maxwell elements in parallel, each element being characterized by a spring constant of modulus $E_i$ and a corresponding time of relaxation $\tau_i$. If this model is subjected to a strain $\sigma$ at the time $t = 0$, the total stress at any subsequent time will be

$$S = \sum S_{i0}\, e^{-t/\tau_i} = \sigma \sum E_{i0}\, e^{-t/\tau_i}. \qquad (12.13)$$

The model may be generalized to represent a continuous distribution of relaxation times; in this case the equation for the stress at time $t$ after application of a strain $\sigma$ is

$$S = \int dS = \sigma \int_0^\infty E(\tau)e^{-t/\tau}\, d\tau, \qquad (12.13\,a)$$

where $E(\tau)$ is a distribution function such that $E(\tau)\,d\tau$ represents the contribution to the total spring constant or elastic modulus of those mechanisms whose relaxation times fall within the interval $\tau$ to $\tau+d\tau$.

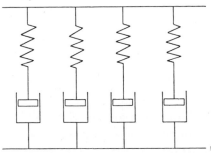

FIG. 12.11.   Maxwell elements in parallel.

*Equivalence of Maxwell and Kelvin systems*

Instead of a number of Maxwell elements in parallel, we might have chosen the alternative system consisting of a number of Kelvin elements in series. Actually it makes little difference from which model we start, since it may be shown that the two types of representation are mathematically equivalent, provided that one is allowed to include at least one 'degenerate' element of either kind, i.e. an element with either the spring or the dashpot missing. This means including an element with either zero or infinite relaxation time. This possibility is automatically included by formulating the problem in terms of a continuous distribution, extending from $\tau = 0$ to $\tau = \infty$.

The necessity for the inclusion of such degenerate elements can be seen by considering, for example, a material which has the property of reaching a limiting strain after a sufficient time at constant stress—a material, that is, which shows no bulk flow. It is obvious that a material of such a kind cannot be represented by a system of Maxwell elements in parallel (Fig. 12.11) unless at least one of the dashpots has infinite viscosity, i.e. does not exist. Similarly a material showing continuous flow at all times, however great, cannot be represented in terms of a Kelvin model unless at least one of the elements has zero spring constant.

In special cases, Bilmes (1945) and Alfrey and Doty (1945) have shown, for example, that a system containing one Maxwell element and one Kelvin element in series is equivalent to two Maxwell elements in parallel, and have worked out the relation between the elastic and resistive constants for the two models. More generally, Kuhn (1947) has shown that any arrangement of Maxwell elements, some in series and some in parallel, may be reduced to a simple system of Maxwell elements in parallel, while Alfrey and Doty have considered the general mathematical transformations for converting from one type of formulation to another. The possibility of such transformations emphasizes the point already referred to, that no specific correspondence is to be expected between the mathematical terms of the formal model and physical or structural elements in the material.

## 7. The form of the distribution function

The possible applicability of the conception of the distribution of relaxation times is limited by a number of further considerations. Firstly, the question as to whether or not any given material can be represented in this way is one which has to be decided on physical and not on purely mathematical grounds, that is to say, either by experiment or from a knowledge of the structure. Secondly, the distribution function, if it exists, may be different for different types of strain, e.g. for extension and shear deformations. Thirdly, it is implied that no structural change, such as crystallization, intervenes in any of the processes considered. Finally, it is assumed that the material has a linear stress-strain relation for an instantaneous strain.

### The early work of Wiechert

In applying the method Wiechert (1893) assumed a distribution function $E(\tau)$ of Gaussian type, when plotted on a *logarithmic* time-scale, i.e. a distribution of the form

$$E(\tau)\,d\tau = Ae^{-b^2z^2}\,dz, \qquad (12.14)$$

where
$$z = \ln(\tau/r),$$

$r$ being the most probable relaxation time. With a suitable choice of the parameter $b$ this function was shown to represent the creep curve of vulcanized rubber much more closely than a single relaxation time.

In more recent times the problem of determining the form of the distribution function has been attacked theoretically by Kirkwood and by Alfrey, and experimentally by Kuhn, Künzle, and Preissmann.

### Kirkwood's theory

Kirkwood's analysis (Kirkwood, 1946) is applicable to a vulcanized rubber, visualized as a network of idealized long-chain molecules, in which the freedom of rotation of individual links is restricted by a resistive force which is a function of the local environment of the chain. The force acting on a link is assumed to be independent of the length of the chain, and proportional to the square of its velocity, and is strictly analogous to the viscous force on a particle in the classical theory of the Brownian motion. The result is expressed in terms of the Kelvin model (which we have seen to be the more appropriate for a material like vulcanized rubber in which there is no continuous flow), that is, in the form of a distribution of retardation times. The distribution function $\Phi(\tau)$ has the property that $\Phi(\tau)\,d\tau$ is the fraction of the total elastic 'compliance' (i.e. reciprocal of modulus) having retardation times in the range $d\tau$. The expression obtained is

$$\Phi(\tau) = \frac{\tau_m}{(\tau + \tau_m)^2}, \tag{12.15}$$

where

$$\tau_m = 2nb^2\zeta_0/kT, \tag{12.15a}$$

$n$ being the number of links in the chain (between points of vulcanization), $b$ the bond length, and $\zeta_0$ the friction constant. The circular frequency at which the loss is a maximum is $\omega_m = 1/\tau_m$, and is therefore inversely proportional to the chain length.

Kirkwood's theory is admittedly only a rather rough approximation, for in the words of the author 'the use of Stokes' law with an effective viscosity coefficient for estimating $\zeta_0$ and $\tau_0$

can scarcely be defended, although such an estimate is adequate in order of magnitude for a polymer chain dispersed in a low molecular weight solvent.'

### Alfrey's theory

The theory proposed by Alfrey (1944), unlike that of Kirkwood, is applicable to an unvulcanized rubber or long-chain polymer in which the molecules are not cross-linked. Alfrey bases his analysis on the consideration that in a randomly-kinked chain the approach to the equilibrium form, on the application or removal of the stress, will take place at a rate depending on the length of chain concerned. Thus the approach to equilibrium will take place most rapidly for very short-chain segments, less rapidly for segments of intermediate length, and least rapidly for very long segments, comparable with the length of the molecule itself. By introducing certain reasonable assumptions he is able to write down an expression representing the contribution to the equilibrium strain (under the action of a constant stress) due to chain segments of any particular length. To find the *rate* of approach to the equilibrium state the arbitrary assumption is made that the retardation time $\tau$ to be associated with a given segment is related to its length in the same way as the bulk viscosity of a linear polymer is related to molecular length, i.e. by Flory's formula (p. 204), so that

$$\tau = A e^{b\sqrt{n}} e^{\Delta E/RT}. \qquad (12.16)$$

The resultant distribution of *retardation* times is then found to be of the form

$$J(\tau)\,d\tau = \frac{2}{5b^2\rho kT} \left( \frac{\ln\tau - \ln A - \Delta E/RT}{\tau} \right) d\tau \qquad (12.17)$$

$$\text{for } \alpha < \ln\tau < \beta,$$

where

$$\alpha = \ln A + \Delta E/RT; \qquad \beta = \ln A + \Delta E/RT + b\sqrt{n}.$$

$J(\tau)$ is the fractional elastic 'compliance' corresponding to retardation times in the range $d\tau$. The distribution extends from the lower limit $\alpha$ to the upper limit $\beta$, the total 'spread' increasing with chain length. Increasing the temperature has the effect of displacing the whole distribution to a lower range of $\tau$.

### The experiments of Kuhn, Künzle, and Preissmann

Very little experimental work has yet appeared in the literature on the subject of the distribution of relaxation times, and data are not available which could usefully be compared with the forms of distribution function predicted by Kirkwood or Alfrey's theories. A serious attack on this problem from the experimental side has, however, recently been made by Kuhn, Künzle, and Preissmann (1947), who utilized measurements of creep under constant load to derive the form of the distribution function, and applied this function to predict the behaviour under oscillatory conditions.

The experiments which were originally used were those carried out by Brenschede (1943), who used a photographic method of recording the deformation of the test piece as a function of time under the action of a compressive load. By using a trigger-operated spring loading, reliable readings of deformation were obtained down to times of only $10^{-2}$ seconds from the application of the stress, and the total range of times investigated was from $10^{-2}$ to $10^4$ seconds.

Over this range the relation between the strain $\sigma$ (measured by $\Delta l/l$) and $\log t$ was found to be linear, and could be expressed in the form

$$\sigma/S = (a+\ln t)/b, \qquad (12.18)$$

$S$ being the stress and $a$ and $b$ constants.

The next step was to derive the distribution of relaxation times corresponding to this law of deformation. The analysis carried out by Kuhn, Künzle, and Preissmann leads to a result which, over the range of $\tau$ covered by the data, is approximately of the form of a rectangular hyperbola, i.e.

$$E(\tau)\,d\tau = \frac{b}{a^2}\frac{d\tau}{\tau}, \qquad (12.19)$$

where $E(\tau)\,d\tau$ is the fraction of the total Young's modulus corresponding to *Maxwell* relaxation times in the range $d\tau$.

Applying this result to the calculation of the dynamic shear modulus $G(\omega)$ and dynamic viscosity $\eta(\omega)$ in a sinusoidal shear deformation, they arrive at the following approximate expressions:

$$G(\omega) = \frac{1}{2(1+\mu)} \frac{b}{a} \tag{12.20\,a}$$

$$\eta(\omega) = \frac{1}{2(1+\mu)} \frac{b}{a^2} \frac{\pi}{2\omega}, \tag{12.20\,b}$$

where $G(\omega)$ and $\eta(\omega)$ are defined as the values of elastic and resistive constants in the equivalent two-element Kelvin model. The factor $1/2(1+\mu)$ is introduced to convert from compressive to shear strain, the value of Poisson's ratio $\mu$ for rubber being approximately 0·5. (This transformation is of course only valid for small strains.) The equations (12.20 a) and (12.20 b) show (a) that the dynamic modulus should be independent of frequency, and (b) that the dynamic viscosity should be inversely proportional to the frequency.

We have already seen that these two conclusions have been confirmed by a number of experimental investigations, for example by those of Dillon, Prettyman, and Hall. These investigations may therefore be regarded as corroborative evidence in favour of the distribution function (12.19). Kuhn and Künzle have gone farther, however, and compared the calculated numerical values of dynamic modulus and dynamic viscosity derived from creep data with the experimental values under oscillatory conditions (Kuhn and Künzle, 1947). Free torsional oscillations of long period (5 to 35 sec.) were employed, and the comparison was made with both tensile and torsional (shear) creep data. Agreement to within the experimental error (5 per cent.) was obtained in the case of the torsional creep data, but differences up to 15 per cent. were found in comparing the torsional oscillation and tensile creep data, showing that the distribution function is specific to the type of strain employed, as might be expected. They showed also that the resistive term was independent of the amplitude of oscillation, but was approximately proportional to the period, so that the product $\eta\omega$ was approximately constant.

## 8. Conclusion

It may be desirable in conclusion to refer again to some of the interpretations of dynamic properties, and to see how they are related to one another. In the last chapter, when dealing with the work of Tobolsky and Andrews, we saw that a vulcanized rubber showed two independent ranges of relaxation, one in the short-time region, related to the breaking of secondary cohesions, and the other in the long-time region, related to scission of the primary network bonds. This second type of process was shown to be capable in certain cases of representation in terms of a relaxation time. This is the only type of process which has been shown to be governed by a single relaxation time. The phenomena dealt with in vibration experiments are not concerned with this process, but with the secondary cohesions between chains. There is therefore no inconsistency between the single relaxation-time phenomena of Tobolsky and Andrews and the continuous distribution of relaxation times derived by Kuhn and Künzle. This illustrates the important point that the function deduced by Kuhn and Künzle to represent this distribution cannot be extrapolated to times outside the range covered by the experiments on which it is based, nor can it be applied to other materials, or to the same material at other temperatures. Their analysis certainly shows that the existence of a definite dynamic modulus and dynamic viscosity does not necessarily imply a single, or even a most probable time of relaxation, but it does not follow that the distribution function $E(\tau)$ may not have a maximum in the region of times below $10^{-2}$ seconds at room temperature, or at correspondingly longer times at lower temperatures. Indeed, it seems quite probable that this is the case, and that the form of the distribution function given by Kuhn, Künzle, and Preissmann may represent only the 'tail' of the complete distribution function. The important conclusions arrived at by these authors in any case do not conflict with Aleksandrov and Lazurkin's interpretation of their experimental data, which were concerned with lower temperatures. They do, however, suggest that caution should be exercised in accepting interpretations of these and other experiments in terms of single relaxation times, and indicate the desirability of further investigations into the form of the relaxation-time spectrum, covering a range of temperatures and also a more extended time-scale than that employed in this pioneer investigation.

# CHAPTER XIII

# THE SOLUTION OF PROBLEMS INVOLVING LARGE ELASTIC STRAINS

## 1. Introduction

IN the present chapter we take up once more the discussion of the purely elastic behaviour of rubber from the point at which we left it in Chapter VII. Having established the fundamental physical laws of the elasticity of rubber-like materials (at least approximately), our further aim is to build up mathematical methods for the solution of particular problems of the kind encountered in engineering applications of rubber. It would not be appropriate, in a book of this character, to discuss the mathematical methods which have been developed in detail; we shall limit ourselves, therefore, to a few selected examples of typical problems which have been successfully handled. These will be sufficient to give some idea of the power and scope of the methods, and the kind of phenomena encountered in large elastic deformations. It is hoped that such a treatment will encourage those who are more particularly interested to follow up the original literature of the subject.

It is perhaps a tribute to the success of the classical theory of elasticity, which forms the basis of engineering practice, that one seldom pauses to consider or to question the validity of the physical basis upon which this elaborate mathematical structure ultimately rests. But, as with any other science, this basis had first to be discovered by observation of the behaviour of matter. It may be expressed in the form of two fundamental postulates: (1) the principle of superposition of stresses and strains, which states that the total strain produced in a body by a number of simultaneously applied stresses is the sum of the strains which would be produced if each of these stresses acted alone,† and (2) the generalized form of Hooke's law, which states that the components of the stress are linear functions of the components of strain.

† Not to be confused with Boltzmann's Superposition Principle (p. 209).

It is found by experiment that, for all those materials which are normally called elastic, these two laws apply with sufficient accuracy, provided that the maximum strain is small.  In practice, this usually implies that the strain should not exceed about 1 per cent. of the undeformed dimensions of the body. Most of the materials of importance in structural engineering either break or show plastic yielding if strained much beyond this point; hence, for engineering purposes, the classical theory of elasticity is entirely adequate.  With rubbers, however, we enter an entirely new field, in which substantially elastic strains of several hundred per cent. are encountered, and with strains of this magnitude the classical theory was not designed to cope. The difficulty is quite fundamental.  We have already seen that Hooke's law does not apply to rubber in simple elongation or compression, and that in general the stresses are non-linear functions of the strains.  It follows that the principle of super-position, of which Hooke's law is a particular case, cannot apply either.  Hence, neither of the fundamental postulates of the classical theory is applicable to rubber-like materials, except in the limiting (and relatively unimportant) case when the strains are very small.

The development of a more general theory of large elastic deformations to replace the classical theory must include (1) a physical basis or law expressing the fundamental properties of the material, and (2) a mathematical technique for working out the consequences of this law in detail in engineering problems.  So far as rubber is concerned, the first aspect of this development has already been considered in earlier chapters, in which we have discussed the stored-energy function, and the fundamental stress-strain relationships for a rubber in a pure homogeneous strain.  The second aspect—the development of mathematical methods for the solution of problems involving strains which are neither pure nor homogeneous—is the one which is the particular concern of the present chapter.

Many aspects of these mathematical developments are, of course, independent of the form of the fundamental stress-strain relationships of the material, and therefore the general theory has applications to materials other than rubber. In these general aspects important contributions to the subject have been made by E. and F. Cosserat (1896), Brillouin (1925), Hencky (1931), Weissenberg (1935), and Murnaghan (1937). We shall here be concerned more particularly with the application of the theory to rubber-like materials, in which connexion it will be convenient to refer particularly to the work of Rivlin, who has dealt not only with the general theory but also with its specific application to rubbers.

## 2. Uniqueness of solution

As a suitable basis for this application, Rivlin has considered in some detail the behaviour of an incompressible material whose fundamental properties are defined by the stored-energy function derived from the statistical theory,

$$W = \tfrac{1}{2}G(\lambda_1^2 + \lambda_2^2 + \lambda_3^2 - 3),  \qquad (13.1)$$

which represents the work of deformation per unit volume in terms of the three principal extension ratios $\lambda_1, \lambda_2, \lambda_3$, in a pure, homogeneous strain. Materials governed by this law, and which are also incompressible, have been designated by Rivlin (1948 $a$) 'neo-Hookean' materials. With such materials, on account of the incompressibility condition, the stresses required to maintain a homogeneous strain are indeterminate to the extent of an arbitrary hydrostatic pressure (eqn. 4.11 $a$); in other words, if the strains are specified, there is no unique solution for the stresses.

Rivlin (1948 $a$) has examined the converse problem of whether there is a unique solution for the strains under specified conditions of stress. He considers a block of rubber in the form of a unit cube to which forces are applied normally to the three pairs of opposite surfaces in three mutually perpendicular directions (Fig. 4.1). Two cases are examined: ($a$) in which the principal stresses, or forces per unit area, *measured in the strained state*, are specified, and ($b$) in which the forces per unit area, *measured in the unstrained state*, are specified. If $t_1$, $t_2$, and $t_3$ are the principal stresses and $f_1$, $f_2$, and $f_3$ the corresponding forces, referred to the unstrained areas, then $t_1 = \lambda_1 f_1$, etc. In

the state of equilibrium, the relations which have to be satisfied
are (from 4.11 a),

$$\left. \begin{aligned} \lambda_1 f_1 = t_1 = G\lambda_1^2 + p \\ \lambda_2 f_2 = t_2 = G\lambda_2^2 + p \\ \lambda_3 f_3 = t_3 = G\lambda_3^2 + p. \end{aligned} \right\} \qquad (13.2)$$

Rivlin has shown that the problem (a) always admits of a unique
solution. Problem (b), on the other hand, may or may not have
a unique solution, according to the conditions. Firstly, if one or
more of the forces are directed inwards (i.e. are compressive) or
are of zero magnitude, the solution is always unique. Secondly,
if all the forces are directed outwards, and if their product
$f_1 f_2 f_3$ is less than $G^3$, the solution is unique. Finally, if all the
forces are directed outwards, and if $f_1 f_2 f_3$ is greater than $G^3$,
there are in general a number of alternative solutions, each of
which satisfies equations (13.2).

These conclusions show that it is only when all the forces are
tensile and large that the possibility of multiple solutions arises.
In the classical theory, the assumption that the strains are
small automatically ensures the uniqueness of the solution, and
in any case it would not be possible to apply to an ordinary
hard solid stresses which would be large enough for their product
to be greater than $G^3$. It is only with soft materials such as
rubbers or jellies that this condition could conceivably be
realized. Even so, its practical realization might be very difficult to accomplish, since this would involve the application of
three sets of tensile forces to the opposite faces of a cuboid.

The physical significance of the multiplicity of solutions may
be better understood by the consideration of a numerical
example. Suppose we take a unit cube of a material for which
$G$ in equations (13.1) and (13.2) has the value 1·0, and apply
to respective pairs of opposite faces normal tensile forces $f_1$, $f_2$,
and $f_3$ of magnitude 4·0, 5·0, and 6·0. For these numerical
values the parabolic relations (13.2) have the form represented
in Fig. 13.1, in which $p$ is plotted as a function of $\lambda$. The condition for incompressibility ($\lambda_1 \lambda_2 \lambda_3 = 1$) has also to be satisfied.
To solve the problem graphically it is only necessary to find

a value of $p$ such that the product of the three $\lambda$'s is unity. The interest of the problem lies in the observation that the line $p = p_1$ cuts each parabola in two places. It is therefore possible to obtain solutions of various types, according to the various combinations of left-handed and right-handed intersections.

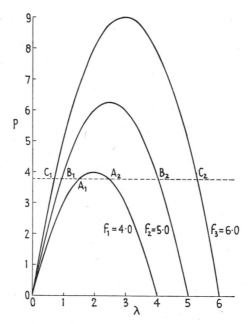

FIG. 13.1. Method of solving for the $\lambda$'s, given the forces $f_1$, $f_2$, and $f_3$.

In the chosen numerical example there are in all seven solutions, which are listed in Table I. Not all of these solutions, however, represent physically stable states. An examination of the question of their stability, using the criteria worked out by Rivlin, shows that in fact only the solutions numbered 2, 3, and 4 in the table are stable, i.e. physically realizable. Which of these three would actually be obtained in a particular experiment would depend on the order in which the forces were applied.

This example serves to illustrate how very much more complicated problems involving large deformations are than similar

Table I

*Multiple solutions for strains*

Unit cube subjected to tensile forces $f_1 = 4{\cdot}0$, $f_2 = 5{\cdot}0$, $f_3 = 6{\cdot}0$. $G = 1{\cdot}0$.

| Solution No. | $p$ | $\lambda_1$ | $\lambda_2$ | $\lambda_3$ |
|---|---|---|---|---|
| 1 | 3·768 | 1·518 | 0·9245 | 0·7126 |
| 2 | 0·1334 | 0·03364 | 4·973 | 5·978 |
| 3 | 0·2016 | 3·947 | 0·04248 | 5·965 |
| 4 | 0·3072 | 3·922 | 4·938 | 0·05164 |
| 5 | 2·779 | 3·105 | 0·6366 | 0·5059 |
| 6 | 2·051 | 0·6040 | 4·549 | 0·3640 |
| 7 | 1·691 | 0·4805 | 0·3648 | 5·703 |

problems in which the deformations are small. The extra complexity is due partly to the fact that the stresses are not determined solely by the forces applied (as they are very nearly in the classical theory) but also by the strains; consequently the solutions reveal little direct connexion between the forces and the corresponding extension ratios.

Although these conclusions have not been experimentally verified, there is little doubt that they would be verified if they could be put to the test, for, as we have seen, the fundamental cause of the multiplicity of solutions is the variation of stress with area, when the force is constant. The phenomenon is therefore not likely to be sensitive to the exact form of the stress-strain relations.

## 3. Inhomogeneous strain

In a pure homogeneous strain, lines which were originally parallel to the directions of the three principal extensions remain unchanged in direction in the strained state. These three directions are the directions of the three principal axes of the strain ellipsoid. In a homogeneous strain which is not pure, on the other hand, the principal axes of the strain ellipsoid do not coincide with the directions of the corresponding lines in the unstrained state; a strain which is not pure is therefore equivalent to a pure strain together with a rotation. Since, however, no work is involved in rotating a strained body, the stored-energy function $W$, defined with respect to a pure strain, is sufficient to determine the elastic stresses in this more general case also.

If the strain is not homogeneous, both the magnitude and the direction of the axes of the strain ellipsoid vary from point to point of the body. However, the strain in the immediate neighbourhood of any given point may be considered to be substantially homogeneous, hence, by working with small elements the equations governing the stress-strain behaviour in a homogeneous strain may still be applied. Since, however, the principal axes of the strain ellipsoid no longer correspond to a fixed direction in space, it is desirable to refer the strain at any point to a fixed coordinate system rather than to the local axes of strain. The state of strain is then determined by the partial differentials of the displacement of the point with respect to the coordinates. If a point initially at $x$, $y$, $z$ is displaced to the position $x+u$, $y+v$, $z+w$, these partial differentials are $\partial u/\partial x$, $\partial u/\partial y$, $\partial u/\partial z$, $\partial v/\partial x$,..., etc.

*Components of stress*

In dealing with pure homogeneous strains we have been concerned only with the three principal stresses, which act normally on surfaces perpendicular to the principal axes of the strain ellipsoid. In the more general case the *traction*, or force per unit area, acting across any plane section through the body, can be resolved into three components, one normal and two tangential to the surface. For the purpose of definition it is sufficient to consider only planes normal to the coordinate axes. The components of the traction across the plane $x = $ const. may then be written $t_{xx}$, $t_{yx}$, $t_{zx}$, of which the first is the normal component, and the remaining two are tangential components respectively parallel to the $y$ and $z$ axes. Taking planes through the point perpendicular to each of the three coordinate axes in turn, we thus obtain in all nine components of the stress. It may be shown, however (Love, 1934), that

$$t_{xy} = t_{yx}, \qquad t_{yz} = t_{zy}, \qquad t_{zx} = t_{xz},$$

and hence the number of independent components is reduced to six, of which three are normal and three tangential components. These six quantities are defined as the *components of stress* at the point.

The relation between the components of stress and the differentials of the displacement is governed by the form of the stored-energy function. For the stored-energy function derived from the statistical theory (eqn. 13.1), Rivlin (1948 a) has deduced the following relations between the components of stress and the strain-differentials:

$$t_{xx} = G\left[\left(1+\frac{\partial u}{\partial x}\right)^2 + \left(\frac{\partial u}{\partial y}\right)^2 + \left(\frac{\partial u}{\partial z}\right)^2\right] + p,$$

$$t_{xy} = G\left[\left(1+\frac{\partial u}{\partial x}\right)\frac{\partial v}{\partial x} + \left(1+\frac{\partial v}{\partial y}\right)\frac{\partial u}{\partial y} + \frac{\partial u}{\partial z}\frac{\partial v}{\partial z}\right],$$

$$\text{(13.3)}$$

with corresponding expressions for $t_{yy}$, $t_{zz}$, $t_{yz}$, and $t_{zx}$.

## 4. Simple shear

The case of pure shear has already been considered in Chapter V. Simple shear (in spite of its name) is rather more compli-

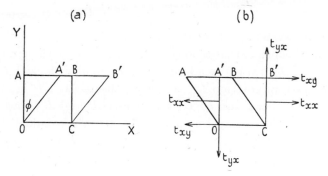

FIG. 13.2. The stresses in a large simple shear. *ABCO*, unstrained state, *A'B'CO*, strained state.

cated, because it is a strain which is not pure. Simple shear is defined (Love, 1934) as a sliding of planes which are perpendicular to *OY* in a direction parallel to *OX* by an amount proportional to their distance from *OX* (Fig. 13.2 (a)). It is customary to measure the amount of the shear by the displacement divided by the distance from *OX*, i.e. by the tangent of the angle $\phi$ through which a line originally parallel to $OY$ is rotated, thus

$$\sigma = AA'/AO = \tan\phi. \tag{13.4}$$

The partial differentials of the displacement of any point are obviously

$$\frac{\partial u}{\partial y} = \sigma; \quad \frac{\partial u}{\partial x} = \frac{\partial u}{\partial z} = \frac{\partial v}{\partial x} = \frac{\partial v}{\partial y} = \frac{\partial v}{\partial z} = \frac{\partial w}{\partial x} = \frac{\partial w}{\partial y} = \frac{\partial w}{\partial z} = 0.$$

Hence, from (13.3) the components of stress are given by the following expressions:

$$\left. \begin{aligned} t_{xx} &= G(1+\sigma^2)+p = G\sigma^2+p' \\ t_{yy} &= t_{zz} = p' \\ t_{xy} &= t_{yx} = G\sigma \\ t_{yz} &= t_{zy} = t_{zx} = t_{xz} = 0, \end{aligned} \right\} \tag{13.5}$$

where $p'$ is an arbitrary constant.

For a particular solution let us choose $p' = 0$. The only stress components which differ from zero are then

$$t_{xx} = G\sigma^2; \quad t_{xy} = t_{yx} = G\sigma. \tag{13.5a}$$

This stress system is illustrated in Fig. 13.2 (b) which represents a simple shear such that a body having the form of the parallelogram $ABCO$ is transformed into the rectangular block $A'B'CO$. The tangential traction $t_{xy}$ acting on the faces $A'B'$ and $OC$, and the equal traction $t_{yx}$ on the faces $OA'$ and $B'C$, are proportional to the shear strain $\sigma$, exactly as in the classical theory for small strains, the constant of proportionality $G$ being formally identical with the modulus of rigidity. But, in addition to these quasi-classical stress-components there is a stress-component $t_{xx}$, proportional to the square of the strain, acting normally on the faces $OA'$ and $B'C$, and which has no counterpart in the classical theory. When the strain is small this component is negligible compared with the tangential stress-components, and the solution reduces to the classical form, but when the strain is large it may easily exceed in magnitude the tangential component. Thus, *a large simple shear cannot be produced by a shear stress acting alone.*

This very important conclusion serves as a typical example of the kind of phenomena to be expected in connexion with large elastic deformations. In most of the problems concerned with large strains (some of which are referred to below) the solution yields stress-components of two types, of which the first is proportional to the strain and reduces to the classical solution when the strain is small, while the second is proportional to the square of the strain, and has no counterpart in the classical solution.

## 5. Torsion of a cylinder

Suppose a cylinder of radius $a$ and height $l$ to be twisted in such a way that the top surface is rotated through an angle $\theta = \psi l$ with respect to the lower surface, the height $l$ remaining unchanged (Fig. 13.3). What forces have to be applied to maintain this strain?

This problem has been analysed by Rivlin (1948 c) for the special case of an incompressible material having a stored-energy function of the Mooney form

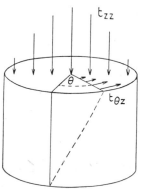

Fig. 13.3.  Torsion of solid cylinder.

$$W = C_1(\lambda_1^2+\lambda_2^2+\lambda_3^2-3)+C_2(1/\lambda_1^2+1/\lambda_2^2+1/\lambda_3^2-3),   (13.6)$$

which includes the neo-Hookean material as a special case ($C_2 = 0$). Rivlin's solution shows that the torsion can be maintained by forces applied to the end surfaces of the cylinder only. These forces are of two kinds:

(1) an azimuthal traction $t_{\theta z}$ proportional to the angle of twist, i.e.

$$t_{\theta z} = 2\psi r(C_1+C_2),     (13.7\,a)$$

and (2) a normal traction $t_{zz}$, proportional to the square of the angle of twist, i.e.

$$t_{zz} = -\psi^2[2a^2 C_2+(a^2-r^2)(C_1-2C_2)].     (13.7\,b)$$

The tangential force (13.7 a) is of the same form as that given by the classical theory for a material whose modulus of rigidity is $2(C_1+C_2)$. The total torque or couple due to this force is

$$T = \pi(C_1+C_2)\psi a^4. \tag{13.7 c}$$

The normal component of stress, on the other hand, has no analogue on the classical theory. If $C_1$ and $C_2$ are positive, this component is always negative, representing a pressure on the

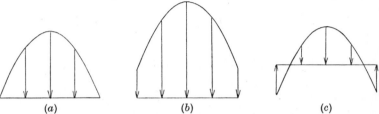

(a)        (b)        (c)

FIG. 13.4. Distribution of pressure over end of cylinder in torsion. (a) Statistical theory. (b) Mooney's theory. (c) Combined extension and torsion.

end surfaces. This pressure is distributed parabolically over the surface, reaching a maximum in the centre. The distribution is illustrated in Fig. 13.4, in which (b) represents the general case, while (a) represents the special case of $C_2 = 0$.

The presence and the distribution of the normal traction on the end face of a vulcanized rubber cylinder has been examined experimentally by Rivlin (1947). The cylinder was bonded on to metal end-plates in which holes had been drilled at five different radial distances from the centre. On twisting the cylinder in such a way that the ends remained at their initial distance apart the rubber was observed to bulge out into the holes, showing that a pressure was being exerted by the rubber on the end-plate. The height of the bulge, $d$, which was taken as approximately proportional to the pressure, was found to be proportional to $\theta^2$, for each value of $r$, in agreement with equation (13.7 b). The ratio $d/\theta^2$ depended on the radial distance from the centre, as shown in Fig. 13.5, where this ratio is plotted against $a^2-r^2$. If the statistical formula (13.1) were applicable the points plotted in this way should lie on a straight line through the origin. Actually they are seen to lie on a line which intersects the vertical axis well above the origin, which is what would be expected from the Mooney formula (13.6), i.e.

when $C_2$ in equation (13.7 $b$) is not zero. The ratio of the slope to the intercept of this line on the vertical axis enables the ratio $C_2/C_1$ to be determined; the value obtained in this way from Rivlin's data was 0·14.

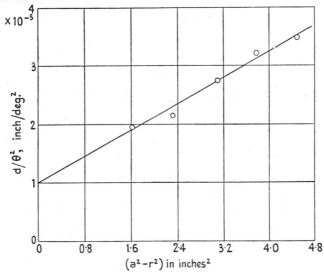

FIG. 13.5. Pressure distribution over end of cylinder in torsion. (Rivlin, 1947.)

## 6. Simultaneous extension and torsion of a cylinder

The next problem dealt with by Rivlin (1948 $b$) is that of the simultaneous extension (or compression) and torsion of a cylinder. Let the original height $l$ be increased or reduced to $\lambda l$, and let $\theta$ be the angle of twist of the upper surface with respect to the lower; the torsion per unit length of the extended (or compressed) cylinder is then $\psi = \theta/\lambda l$. By virtue of the incompressibility, a point initially at a distance $r$ from the axis will, in the deformed state, be at a distance $r_1 = r\lambda^{-\frac{1}{2}}$. The solution to this problem, *for a body governed by the statistical formula* (13.1), shows, as before, that the specified strain may be maintained by forces applied to the end surfaces only. These forces are

(1) an azimuthal tangential traction (per unit area of the deformed surface) given by

$$t_{\theta z} = G\lambda^2\psi r_1, \tag{13.8 a}$$

and (2) a normal traction

$$t_{zz} = G(\lambda^2 - 1/\lambda) - \tfrac{1}{2}G\lambda^2\psi^2(a_1^2 - r_1^2), \tag{13.8 b}$$

where $a_1$ $(= a\lambda^{-\frac{1}{2}})$ is the radius of the deformed cylinder. The traction $t_{zz}$ is the sum of two terms, of which the first, $G(\lambda^2 - 1/\lambda)$, is simply the stress required to extend the cylinder in the absence of the torsion, while the second represents a compressive force proportional to the square of the torsion. If $\lambda < 1$, corresponding to a compression, the resultant total force is compressive at all points, but if $\lambda > 1$, corresponding to an extension, the total force is, for the smaller extensions, tensile over a peripheral region and compressive over a central region (Fig. 13.4 (c)), and for the larger extensions, tensile at all points. The total torque on the end surface due to the azimuthal traction is

$$T = \tfrac{1}{2}\pi G\psi a^4, \tag{13.9 a}$$

i.e. the same whether or not the cylinder is extended. The total tensile force is

$$f = \pi Ga^2(\lambda - 1/\lambda^2) - \tfrac{1}{4}\pi G\psi^2 a^4, \tag{13.9 b}$$

which may be either positive or negative, according to the relative values of $\psi$ and $\lambda$.

## 7. Torsion of a hollow cylinder

The problem of the torsion of a hollow cylinder is rather more

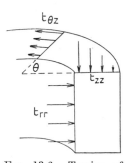

FIG. 13.6. Torsion of hollow cylinder.

difficult. It has been shown by Rivlin (1948 b) that a state of torsion cannot now be maintained by the application of forces to the end faces only, but that additional forces have to be applied to one or other of the curved surfaces. In a particular solution a compressive traction is applied to the inner curved surface (Fig. 13.6), while no forces are applied to the outer curved surface. The magnitude of this compressive traction is

$$t_{rr} = \tfrac{1}{2}G\psi^2(a^2 - b^2). \tag{13.10}$$

For this particular solution the forces on the end faces are a tangential traction $t_{\theta z}$ and a normal traction $t_{zz}$, given by the formulae (13.7 $a$) and (13.7 $b$) respectively (with $C_2 = 0$ and $2C_1 = G$).

## 8. Conclusion

The examples quoted are sufficient to indicate the general lines of development of methods for the handling of problems involving large elastic deformations. The solutions have been worked out on the basis of a particular stored-energy function, but the kind of result obtained would not be seriously altered by an alternative choice of this function, though the numerical details would of course require modification. We may therefore feel that the effects to which attention has been drawn in this chapter are quite fundamental, and are likely to prove of considerable practical interest. Since this chapter was written the subject has been further developed and extended, and it may well be that we are here witnessing the emergence of a new branch of engineering—the engineering of rubber-like materials—evolved from the happy combination of the study of rubber from the molecular standpoint with the general mathematical theory of elasticity.

# BIBLIOGRAPHY†

ALEKSANDROV and LAZURKIN. *J. tech. Phys. U.S.S.R.* 1939, **9**, 1249; *Rubb. Chem. & Technol.* 1940, **13**, 886.

ALFREY. *J. chem. Phys.* 1944, **12**, 374.

—— and DOTY. *J. appl. Phys.* 1945, **16**, 700.

ANTHONY, CASTON, and GUTH. *J. phys. Chem.* 1942, **46**, 826; *Rubb. Chem. & Technol.* 1943, **16**, 297.

BEKKEDAHL. *Bur. Stand. J. Res., Wash.* 1934, **13**, 410; *Rubb. Chem. & Technol.* 1935, **8**, 5.

—— and WOOD, 1941*a*. *Industr. Engng. Chem.* 1941, **33**, 381; *Rubb. Chem. & Technol.* 1941, **14**, 347.

—— —— 1941*b*. *J. chem. Phys.* 1941, **9**, 193; *Rubb. Chem. & Technol.* 1941, **14**, 544.

BENOÎT. *J. chim. Phys.* 1947, **44**, 18.

BILMES. *J. sci. Instrum.* 1945, **22**, 16.

BLOOMFIELD. *J. polymer Sci.* 1946, **1**, 312; *Rubb. Chem. & Technol.* 1947, **20**, 360.

BRENSCHEDE. *Kolloidzschr.* 1943, **104**, 1.

BRILLOUIN. *Ann. Phys., Paris*, 1925, **3**, 251.

BUNN. *Trans. Faraday Soc.* 1939, **35**, 482.

—— *Proc. roy. Soc.* 1942, A **180**, 40; *Rubb. Chem. & Technol.* 1942, **15**, 709.

—— *Advances in Colloid Science*, II, 1946. Interscience Publishers (N.Y.), p. 109.

—— and ALCOCK. *Trans. Faraday Soc.* 1945, **40**, 317.

BURGERS. *First Report on Viscosity and Plasticity*, 1939 (Amsterdam), chap. 1.

BUSSE. *J. phys. Chem.* 1932, **36**, 2862; *Rubb. Chem. & Technol.* 1934, **7**, 273.

COSSERAT, E., and COSSERAT, F. *Ann. Fac. Sci. Toulouse*, 1896, **10**, 1.

DART, ANTHONY, and GUTH. *Industr. Engng. Chem.* 1942, **34**, 1340; *Rubb. Chem. & Technol.* 1943, **16**, 178.

DENBIGH. *Trans. Faraday Soc.* 1940, **36**, 936.

DILLON and JOHNSTON. *Physics*, 1933, **4**, 225; *Rubb. Chem. & Technol.* 1934, **7**, 248.

—— PRETTYMAN, and HALL. *J. appl. Phys.* 1944, **15**, 309; *Rubb. Chem. & Technol.* 1944, **17**, 597.

DOW. *J. chem. Phys.* 1939, **7**, 201.

ELLIOTT and LIPPMANN. *J. appl. Phys.* 1945, **16**, 50; *Rubb. Chem. & Technol.* 1945, **18**, 579.

EYRING. *Phys. Rev.* 1932, **39**, 746.

† References to *Rubber Chemistry and Technology* relate to reprints or translations of original papers cited.

FARMER and SHIPLEY. *J. polymer Sci.* 1946, **1**, 293; *Rubb. Chem. &
Technol.* 1947, **20**, 341.
FIELD. *J. appl. Phys.* 1941, **12**, 23; *Rubb. Chem. & Technol.* 1941, **14**,
555.
FIKENTSCHER and MARK. *Kautschuk*, 1930, **6**, 2; *Rubb. Chem. & Technol.*
1930, **3**, 201.
FISHER. *Proc. phys. Soc.* 1948, **60**, 99.
FLINT and NAUNTON. *I.R.I. Trans.* 1937, **12**, 367; *Rubb. Chem. &
Technol.* 1937, **10**, 584.
FLORY. *J. Amer. chem. Soc.* 1940, **62**, 1057.
—— *Chem. Rev.* 1944, **35**, 51.
—— *Industr. Engng. Chem.* 1946, **38**, 417; *Rubb. Chem. & Technol.*
1946, **19**, 552.
—— *J. chem. Phys.* 1947, **15**, 397.
—— and REHNER. Ibid. 1943, **11**, 512.
GEE. *Trans. Faraday Soc.* 1946, **42**, 585; *Rubb. Chem. & Technol.* 1947,
**20**, 442.
—— 1947a. *J. polymer Sci.* 1947, **2**, 451.
—— 1947b. *Quart. Rev. Chem. Soc.* 1947, **1**, 265.
—— and TRELOAR. *I.R.I. Trans.* 1940, **16**, 184; *Rubb. Chem. & Technol.*
1941, **14**, 580.
GEHMAN and FIELD. *J. appl. Phys.* 1939, **10**, 564; *Rubb. Chem. & Technol.* 1939, **12**, 706.
—— —— *J. appl. Phys.* 1944, **15**, 371; *Rubb. Chem. & Technol.* 1944,
**17**, 640.
—— WOODFORD, and STAMBAUGH. *Industr. Engng. Chem.* 1941, **33**,
1032; *Rubb. Chem. & Technol.* 1941, **14**, 842.
GIBBONS, GERKE, and TINGEY. *Industr. Engng. Chem. (Anal.)*, 1933,
**5**, 279; *Rubb. Chem. & Technol.* 1933, **6**, 525.
GLASSTONE, LAIDLER, and EYRING. *Theory of Rate Processes*, 1941.
McGraw-Hill (N.Y.).
GOPPEL. *Appl. Sci. Res.* 1946, A **1**, 3. See also Wildschut, 1946, p. 156.
—— 1946a. Reported Wildschut, 1946, p. 163.
GOUGH. *Mem. Lit. Phil. Soc. Manchester*, 1805, **1**, 288.
GREEN and TOBOLSKY. *J. chem. Phys.* 1946, **14**, 80.
GROH and VON HEVESY. *Ann. Phys. Lpz.* 1920, **63**, 85.
GUTH and MARK. *Mh. Chem.* 1934, **65**, 93.
—— and JAMES. *Industr. Engng. Chem.* 1941, **33**, 624; *Rubb. Chem.
& Technol.* 1941, **14**, 596.
—— —— and MARK. *Advances in Colloid Science*, II, 1946. Inter-
science Publishers (N.Y.).
HALL. *Biometrika*, 1927, **19**, 240.
HALLER. *Kolloidzschr.* 1931, **56**, 257.
HAMM. *Onderzoekingen over het rheologisch gedrag van ongevulcaniseerde
rubber met rotatieplastometer*, 1946. Meinema (Delft).
HENCKY. *J. Rheology*, 1931, **2**, 169.

HIRSCHFELDER, STEVENSON, and EYRING. *J. Chem. Phys.* 1937, **5,** 896.

HOCK. *Z. Elektrochem.* 1925, **31,** 404.

HOLT and MCPHERSON. *Bur. Stand. J. Res., Wash.* 1936, **17,** 657;
    *Rubb. Chem. & Technol.* 1937, **10,** 412.

HUNTER and OAKES, *Trans. Faraday Soc.* 1945, **41,** 49.

IRWIN. *Biometrika,* 1927, **19,** 225.

JAMES. *J. chem. Phys.* 1947, **15,** 651.

—— and GUTH. Ibid. 1943, **11,** 455.

—— —— Ibid. 1947, **15,** 669.

JEFFREY. *Trans. Faraday Soc.* 1944, **40,** 517; *Rubb. Chem. & Technol.*
    1945, **18,** 280.

JOULE. *Philos. Trans.* 1859, **149,** 91.

KARRER. *Phys. Rev.* 1932, **39,** 857 (Abstr.); *Protoplasma,* 1933, **18,** 475.

KATZ. *Chem. Z.* 1925, **49,** 353; *Naturwissenschaften,* 1925, **13,** 410;
    *Kolloidzschr.* **36,** 300 and **37,** 19.

KAUZMANN and EYRING. *J. Amer. chem. Soc.* 1940, **62,** 3113.

KELVIN. *Quart. J. Math.* (1855).

KEMP and EGAN. *J. Amer. chem. Soc.* 1938, **60,** 1521.

KIRKWOOD. *J. chem. Phys.* 1946, **14,** 51.

KISTIAKOWSKY, LACHER, and STITT. Ibid. 1939, **7,** 289.

KUHN, W. *Kolloidzschr.* 1934, **68,** 2.

—— Ibid. 1936, **76,** 258.

—— *Z. phys. Chem.* 1939, B **42,** 1.

—— *J. polymer Sci.* 1946, **1,** 380.

—— *Helv. chim. Acta,* 1947, **30,** 487.

—— and GRÜN. *Kolloidzschr.* 1942, **101,** 248.

—— and KUHN, H. *Helv. chim. Acta,* 1943, **26,** 1934.

—— —— Ibid. 1946, **29,** 1095.

—— —— 1946 *a.* Ibid. 1946, **29,** 1634.

—— and KÜNZLE. Ibid. 1947, **30,** 839.

—— —— and PREISSMANN. Ibid. pp. 307 and 464.

LEADERMANN. *Elastic and Creep Properties of Filamentous Materials
    and other High Polymers,* 1943. (Textile Foundation, Wash.)

LOTMAR and MEYER. *Mh. Chem.* 1936, **69,** 115.

LOVE. *The Mathematical Theory of Elasticity,* 1934. Cambridge Uni-
    versity Press.

MACK. *J. Amer. chem. Soc.* 1934, **56,** 2757; *Rubb. Chem. & Technol.*
    1935, **8,** 192.

MCPHERSON. *Bur. Stand. J. Res., Wash.* 1932, **8,** 751; *Rubb. Chem. &*
    *Technol.* 1932, **5,** 523.

MEYER and FERRI. *Helv. chim. Acta,* 1935, **18,** 570; *Rubb. Chem. &*
    *Technol.* 1935, **8,** 319.

—— and VAN DER WYK. *Helv. chim. Acta,* 1946, **29,** 1842.

—— VON SUSICH, and VALKO. *Kolloidzschr.* 1932, **59,** 208.

MOONEY. *Industr. Engng. Chem. (Anal.),* 1934, **6,** 147; *Rubb. Chem.
    & Technol.* 1934, **7,** 564.

MOONEY. *Physics*, 1936, **7**, 413; *Rubb. Chem. & Technol.* 1937, **10**, 214.

—— *J. appl. Phys.* 1940, **11**, 582.

MORSS. *J. Amer. chem. Soc.* 1938, **60**, 237.

MOTT and GURNEY. *Rep. Progr. Phys.* 1938, **5**, 46.

MULLINS. *I.R.I. Trans.* 1947, **22**, 235; *Rubb. Chem. & Technol.* 1947, **20**, 998.

MURNAGHAN. *Amer. J. Math.* 1937, **59**, 235.

ORR. *Trans. Faraday Soc.* 1947, **43**, 12.

OSBORNE, GARNER, and YOST. *J. chem. Phys.* 1940, **8**, 131.

OSTWALD. *Kolloidzschr.* 1926, **40**, 58.

PARK. *Mem. Coll. Sci. Kyoto*, 1939, A **22**, 13; *Rubb. Chem. & Technol.* 1939, **12**, 778.

PETERSON, ANTHONY, and GUTH. *Industr. Engng. Chem.* 1942, **34**, 1349; *Rubb. Chem. & Technol.* 1943, **16**, 290.

PIPER and SCOTT. *J. sci. Instrum.* 1945, **22**, 206; *Rubb. Chem. & Technol.* 1946, **19**, 822.

PITZER. *J. chem. Phys.* 1937, **5**, 469.

RAINE, RICHARDS, and RYDER. *Trans. Faraday Soc.* 1945, **41**, 56.

RIVLIN. *J. appl. Phys.* 1947, **18**, 444.

—— 1948 *a*. *Philos. Trans.* 1948, A **240**, 459 and 491.

—— 1948 *b*. Ibid., p. 509.

—— 1948 *c*. Ibid. A **241**, 379.

ROTH and WOOD. *J. appl. Phys.* 1944, **15**, 749.

SADRON. *J. Chim. phys.* 1946, **43**, 12.

SAUNDERS and TRELOAR. *I.R.I. Trans.* 1948, **24**, 92.

SAUTER. *Z. phys. Chem.* 1937, B **36**, 405.

SCOTT. *I.R.I. Trans.* 1931, **7**, 1.

SCOTT BLAIR. *A Survey of General and Applied Rheology*, 1945, Pitman.

SMALLWOOD. *J. appl. Phys.* 1937, **8**, 505; *Rubb. Chem. & Technol.* 1937, **10**, 690.

SMITH and SAYLOR. *Bur. Stand. J. Res., Wash.* 1938, **21**, 257; *Rubb. Chem. & Technol.* 1939, **12**, 18.

TAMMANN and JENCKEL. *Z. anorg. Chem.* 1930, **193**, 76.

TAYLOR. *J. chem. Phys.* 1947, **15**, 412.

THIBODEAU and McPHERSON. *Bur. Stand. J. Res., Wash.* 1934, **13**, 887; *Rubb. Chem. & Technol.* 1935, **8**, 183.

THIESSEN and KIRSCH. *Naturwissenschaften*, 1938, **26**, 387; *Rubb. Chem. & Technol.* 1939, **12**, 12.

—— —— *Naturwissenschaften*, 1939, **27**, 390; *Rubb. Chem. & Technol.* 1940, **13**, 48.

—— and WITTSTADT. *Z. phys. Chem.* 1938, B **41**, 33; *Rubb. Chem. & Technol.* 1939, **12**, 736.

TOBOLSKY and ANDREWS. *J. chem. Phys.* 1945, **13**, 3; *Rubb. Chem. & Technol.* 1945, **18**, 731.

TRELOAR. *Trans. Faraday Soc.* 1940, **36**, 538; *Rubb. Chem. & Technol.* 1940, **13**, 795.

TRELOAR. *Trans. Faraday Soc.* 1941, **37**, 84; *Rubb. Chem. & Technol.* 1942, **15**, 251.

—— 1943 *a. Trans. Faraday Soc.* 1943, **39**, 36; *Rubb. Chem. & Technol.* 1943, **16**, 746.

—— 1943 *b. Trans. Faraday Soc.* 1943, **39**, 241; *Rubb. Chem. & Technol.* 1944, **17**, 296.

—— 1943 *c. Proc. phys. Soc.* 1943, **55**, 345.

—— 1943 *d. Nature,* 1943, **151**, 616.

—— 1944 *a. Trans. Faraday Soc.* 1944, **40**, 59; *Rubb. Chem. & Technol.* 1944, **17**, 813.

—— 1944 *b. I.R.I. Trans.* 1944, **19**, 201; *Rubb. Chem. & Technol.* 1944, **17**, 957.

—— 1944 *c. Trans. Faraday Soc.* 1944, **40**, 109; *Rubb. Chem. & Technol.* 1944, **17**, 779.

—— 1946 *a. Trans. Faraday Soc.* 1946, **42**, 77; *Rubb. Chem. & Technol.* 1946, **19**, 1002.

—— 1946 *b. Trans. Faraday Soc.* 1946, **42**, 83; *Rubb. Chem. & Technol.* 1946, **19**, 1009.

—— 1947 *a. Trans. Faraday Soc.* 1947, **43**, 277.

—— 1947 *b.* Ibid. 1947, **43**, 284.

—— *Proc. phys. Soc.* 1948, **60**, 135.

TUCKETT. *Trans. Faraday Soc.* 1942, **38**, 310.

WALL. *J. chem. Phys.* 1942, **10**, 485; *Rubb. Chem. & Technol.* 1942, **15**, 806.

—— 1943 *a. J. chem. Phys.* 1943, **11**, 67; *Rubb. Chem. & Technol.* 1943, **16**, 479.

—— 1943 *b. J. chem. Phys.* 1943, **11**, 527; *Rubb. Chem. & Technol.* 1944, **17**, 392.

WEISSENBERG. *Arch. Sci. phys. nat.* 1935, **17**, 1.

WIECHERT. *Wied. Ann. Phys.* 1893, **50**, 335, 546.

WIEGAND and SNYDER. *I.R.I. Trans.* 1934, **10**, 234; *Rubb. Chem. & Technol.* 1935, **8**, 151.

WILDSCHUT. *Technological and Physical Investigations on Natural and Synthetic Rubbers,* 1946. Elsevier (N.Y. and Amsterdam).

WOOD. *Advances in Colloid Science,* II, 1946. Interscience Publishers (N.Y.).

—— BEKKEDAHL, and GIBSON. *J. chem. Phys.* 1945, **13**, 475; *Rubb. Chem. & Technol.* 1946, **19**, 546.

—— and ROTH. *J. appl. Phys.* 1944, **15**, 781; *Rubb. Chem. & Technol.* 1945, **18**, 367.

# AUTHOR INDEX

# SUBJECT INDEX

PRINTED IN
GREAT BRITAIN
AT THE
UNIVERSITY PRESS
OXFORD
BY
CHARLES BATEY
PRINTER
TO THE
UNIVERSITY